John Thompson's Modern Course for the Piano

The First Grade Book
Something New Every Lesson

Verses by
Katherine Faith

Drawings by
Frederick S. Manning

Cover Illustration by
DiLonardo Design

A clear, correct and complete
foundation in the study of the
piano to enable the student to think
and feel musically

The Willis Music Company
Florence, Kentucky 41022-0548

Copyright, MCMXXXVII, by The Willis Music Co.
Printed in U.S.A.

THE PROGRESSIVE SUCCESSION
of
JOHN THOMPSON'S MODERN COURSE FOR THE PIANO
"SOMETHING NEW EVERY LESSON"

PREPARATORY GRADE

Teaching Little Fingers to Play A book for the earliest beginner combining ROTE and NOTE approach.

Teaching Little Fingers to Play More This is a follow-up book to Teaching Little Fingers to Play, to ease the transition into the Modern Course-First Grade Book.

Accompaniment Book : *Teaching Little Fingers to Play Ensemble*

With these accompaniments, teacher, parent, or advanced student may play each piece as a duet. The second piano part is invaluable for two-piano, four-hand playing in class or recital.

GRADE ONE

John Thompson's First Grade Book A correct foundation for teaching the student to think and feel musically.

Hanon Studies (Specially edited by John Thompson) Pages 2-23 (in quarter-notes) to be used for supplementary work.

Supplementary material for diversion:
For Girls Who Play · Covered Wagon Suite
Let's Join the Army · Students Series —Grade 1 Teaching Pieces

GRADE TWO

John Thompson's Second Grade Book Carries on the principles of the course "make haste slowly but learn thoroughly."

Hanon Studies (Specially edited by John Thompson) Pages 24-43 to be used supplementarily.

First Studies in Style

Supplementary material for diversion:
The Pilgrim Suite · Students Series —Grade 2 Teaching Pieces

GRADE THREE

John Thompson's Third Grade Book Progresses uninterruptedly and logically.

Third Grade Velocity Studies (Specially edited by John Thompson)

Hanon Studies—Book Two (Specially edited by John Thompson)

Keyboard Attacks · World Known Melodies

Students Series —Grade 3 Teaching Pieces

FOR SALE BY ALL MUSIC DEALERS

Published by **THE WILLIS MUSIC CO.** Florence, Kentucky 41022-0548

CONTENTS
"Something New Every Lesson"

Page

Foreword 2

1. **Hand Position** *(C Major)* ~ The Phrase "Music Land" 4
2. **Musical Form** ~ "Patterns" 5
3. **Rhythm and Accents** ~ "Runaway River" 6
4. **Tempo** ~ "The Traffic Cop" 7
5. **Tonal Shading** ~ "Swans on the Lake" 8
   Half Steps ~ Sharps, Flats and Natural 10
   Whole Steps ~ Writing Lesson 11
6. **Accidentals** ~ "The Scissors Grinder" 12
7. **New "Hand Position"** (G Major) ~ "A Song of Penny Candy" 13
8. **Two Melody Patterns** ~ "The Man in the Moon" 14
9. **Folk-tunes** ~ "The Party" 15
   Phrasing Attack ~ Right Hand and Left Hand 16
10. **Combining Hand Positions** ~ "The Robin" 17
11. **Finger and Harmony Patterns** ~ "The Merry Clown" 18
12. **Harmony Patterns** *(Left Hand)* ~ "The Cuckoo" 19
    Examination No. 1 20
    Scales ~ Ways and Means 21
    Building the C Major and G Major Scales 22
13. **Ascending Scale in C Major** ~ "Scaling the Wall" 23
14. **Descending Scale in C Major** ~ "The Chimes" 24
15. **New "Hand Position" for Left Hand** ~ "Stepping Stones" 25
    Chord Building ~ Intervals and Triads 26
    Chord Inversions ~ Triads in C Major and F Major 27
16. **Broken Chord as a Melody** ~ "Mountain Climbing" 28
17. **New "Hand Position"** (F Major) ~ "A Chord Frolic" 29
18. **A First Recital Piece** ~ "The Fairies' Harp" ... 30
19. **First Introduction to Eighth Notes** ~ "The Wishing Star" 32
20. **New "Hand Position"** (D Major) ~ "Lightly Row" 33
21. **New "Hand Position"** (A Major) ~ "Little Spring Song" 34
22. **Staccato and Legato Groups** ~ "Falling Leaves" 36
23. **Dance Forms** ~ "Dutch Dance" 37
24. **A Descriptive Recital Piece** ~ "The Fairy Court" 38
    Examination No. 2 39
25. **Example in Staccato** ~ "The Tiresome Woodpecker" 40
26. **Extended "Hand Postion"** *(A Major)* ~ "The Knight and the Lady" 42
27. **Dotted Quarter Notes** ~ "Air from Mozart" 43
28. **Rhythmical Pattern used by Brahms** ~ "A Little Waltz" 44
29. **New "Hand Position"** (B♭ Major) ~ "The Owl's Question" 45
30. **Six-Eight Time** ~ "Cheer for the Blue" 46
31. **Two-note Phrases in 6/8 Time** ~ "The Cuckoo Clock" 47
32. **Six-Eight Time** (G Major) ~ "The Singing Mouse" 48
33. **Hand Position Extended in Left Hand** (*F Major*) ~ "The Birthday Cake" 49
34. **Playing in Two "Hand Positions"** ~ "The Popcorn Man" 50
35. **Two "Hand Positions"** (*6/8 Time*) ~ "The Merry-go-Round" 51
36. **Syncopation** ~ "A Spanish Fiesta" 52
37. **A Hunting Song** ~ "The Fox Hunt" 54
38. **Two "Hand Positions"** ~ "To Celia" 56
    Examination No. 3 57
39. **Cross-Hand Position** ~ "The Frog Chorus" 58
40. **Wrist Staccato** ~ "The Sleigh" 59
41. **New "Hand Position"** (E♭ Major) ~ "Little Bo-Peep" 60
42. **Forearm Attack** ~ "Evening Bells" 62
43. **New "Hand Position"** (E Major) ~ "Peasant Dance" 64
44. **Broken Chord Accompaniment** ~ "Long, Long Ago" 65
45. **Three "Hand Positions"** ~ "Silent Night" 66
46. **Scale Patterns and Chords** ~ "A Keyboard Recreation" 67
47. **Interpreting Characteristic Music** ~ "The Streamliner" 68
48. **New "Hand Position"** (A♭ Major) ~ "To a Skyscraper" 70
49. **Two "Hand Positions"** (*Both Hands*) ~ "Dublin Town" 72
50. **Sixteenth Notes** ~ "John Peel" 74
    Examination No. 4 75
    Technical Drills 76
    FOUR CERTIFICATES OF MERIT 79

Preface

This book is designed for the use of FIRST GRADE students. Perhaps the greatest recommendation for its use is that it "makes haste slowly". Many bad habits which hamper students in the upper grades are to be traced directly to faulty training in the beginning. Thus, many hours of labor and many thousands of dollars are spent annually in the sometimes hopeless task of attempting to correct attitudes, habits, and mistakes that should never have been allowed to take root in the first place. "As the twig is bent, the tree's inclined". This old aphorism applies equally to MUSCULAR CONTROL, TECHNIQUE, TIME PROBLEMS, MUSICAL CONCEPTION, HABITS OF THOUGHT and PRACTICE.

MAKE A SHOWING WITH STUDENTS

It is reasonable to assume that most errors are due less to inattention on the part of the teacher than to an eagerness to SEE THE STUDENT PROGRESS RAPIDLY. Sometimes they may be the fruit of using *wrong material*. A great many early grade books have apparently been written for the exclusive use of "budding geniuses," of whom there are all too few. Yet, even these would benefit immeasurably from a sounder method of learning fundamentals which, in a final analysis, have to be mastered anyway in the end at a great sacrifice of time and energy. The student who thoroughly masters every simple step as it presents itself and learns to play his little compositions cleanly, correctly and UP TO SPEED will make a far better showing than the one who is allowed to stumble in desultory fashion through more technically advanced music.

THIS IS A FIRST GRADE BOOK

Most of the pieces contained in this first grade book are written in five-finger position. Towards the end there are a few examples of one-finger extensions. The book is for the first-grade student of any age and it is assumed that the student has had some preliminary piano work at the preparatory level.

OBJECTIVES

The purpose of this book is to lay a clear, correct and complete foundation for piano study so that the student can THINK and FEEL musically. It is quite possible to teach students of the first grade how to play with musical understanding. Though they play simple melodies and very modest little pianistic patterns, they should be impressed with the fact that these are the bricks, as it were, which, when laid together, build the greatest compositions. If they learn to recognize and perform these small fragments properly and with intelligence, they will, as they progress, meet the larger forms of composition with perfect understanding, and will not be bewildered at the weaving together of many musical fragments into a perfect whole.

THE IMPORTANCE OF PATTERNS

With this in mind, the author lays much stress in this book on MELODY PATTERNS, RHYTHMICAL PATTERNS, HARMONY PATTERNS and FINGER PATTERNS. Any elementary student who learns to recognize patterns is a better sight reader, memorizer, interpreter and, through a knowledge of finger patterns, a better pianist than the child who laboriously learns his compositions note by note. A note by note conception of music is not only antiquated, but apt to lessen interest and retard progress. Do not allow students to acquire this habit if you wish to keep them interested.

Preface (*Contd.*)

FIVE-FINGER POSITIONS

Practically all of the examples in this book remain in the FIVE FINGER POSITION. For this reason TRANSPOSITION IS QUITE EASY by means of *finger patterns*, and the student is given opportunity through ACTUAL EXPERIENCE to develop a real finger sense in five-finger groups before venturing into more complicated fingering. The five-finger group is the basis for scale and arpeggio fingering which follow later. Scales and Arpeggios, of course, are the foundation of all piano technique: Therefore five-finger drills should not be passed over in a superficial manner.

VARIATIONS ON FIVE-FINGER GROUPS

As students become familiar with several five-finger positions (C major, F major, G major, etc.) they are, IN THIS BOOK, gradually introduced to examples combining more than one five-finger group. In other words, they learn that it is no more difficult to change from one five-finger position to another *in the same piece* than it is to do so in two pieces—each one of which requires a different position.

Students are also taught to recognize five-finger groups *with extensions,* that is, with one note added on either side of the group.

Example

These simple extensions can be played without shifting the hands out of position. Such extensions also make it possible to enrich both the melodic and harmonic content of the little examples which ordinarily grow very monotonous when kept strictly within the five-note limit for the entire content of a book.

KEYBOARD ATTACKS

Since the piano is, after all, a mechanical instrument made up of keys, strings, hammers and other mundane materials, all our thoughts and emotions must be produced through it by the mechanical action of these mediums in direct communication with our fingers. The proper TOUCH must be acquired or, regardless of the emotions of the performer, the piano will not respond. Therefore, THE SAME KEYBOARD ATTACKS USED BY THE GREAT ARTISTS SHOULD BE TAUGHT IN MINIATURE TO THE BEGINNER.

Resolve that your students are to have the benefit of such training *now.* In perusing this book you will find that the following touches are definitely stressed: *Finger Legato, Phrasing Attack, Wrist Staccato, Forearm Legato and Staccato.* If properly and carefully applied they will enable beginners to play little pieces with precision, expression and musical understanding. When they have finished the book, students will be ready and eager for their next step up the musical ladder into GRADE TWO. They will have learned to play the piano as a musical instrument and not as a sort of typewriter.

John Thompson

P. S. Certificates of Merit have been included on page 79 as awards for "Examination Reviews" pages 20, 39, 57 and 75.--J.T.

4

Key of C Major

New Hand Position

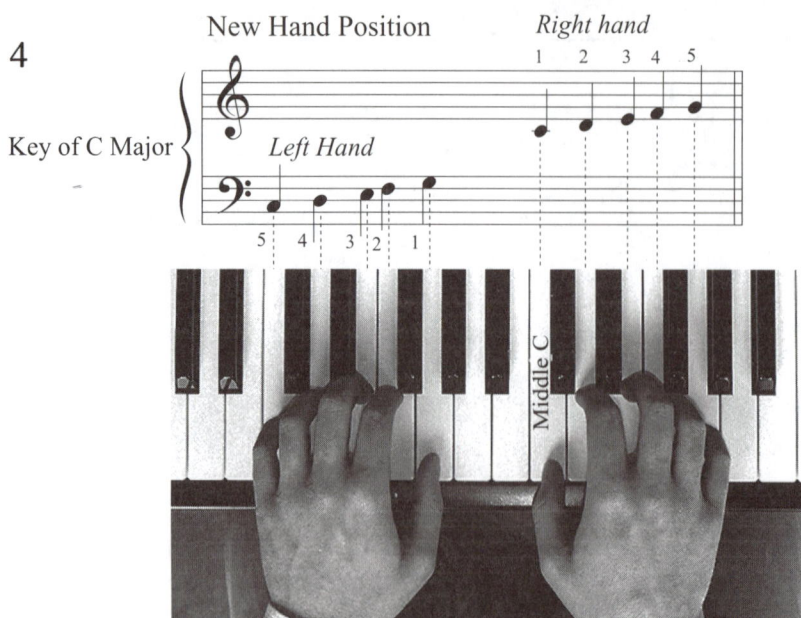

BEFORE beginning to play this piece, PLACE THE HANDS IN THE POSITION shown above. Play each hand separately a few times to get the FEEL of the five finger position in the key of C MAJOR.

1. MUSIC LAND

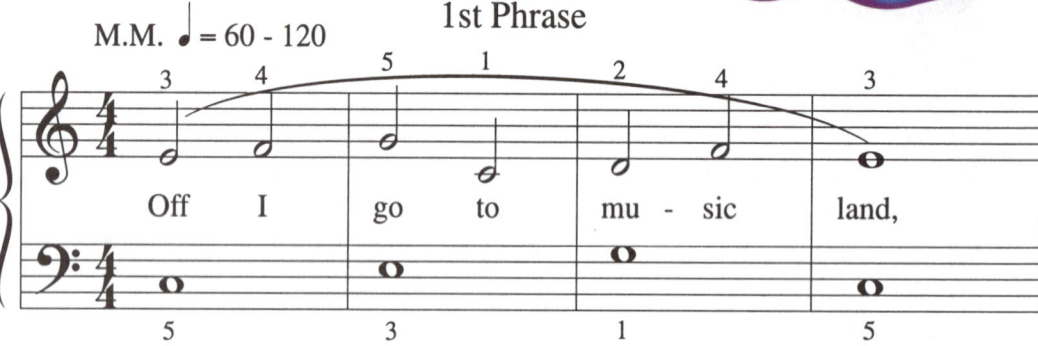

Off I go to mu - sic land,

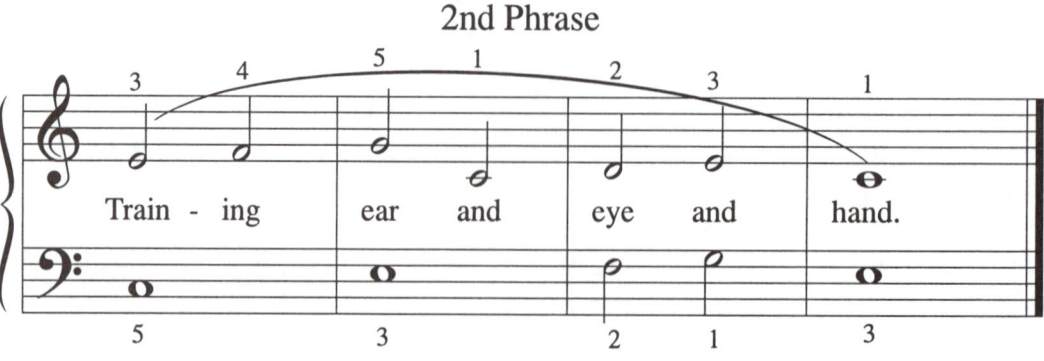

Train - ing ear and eye and hand.

THE PHRASE

Music is a language. It can express thoughts and even tell stories—*musical stories.* When we hear a story we listen *sentence by sentence,* NOT letter by letter. So it is with music. Single notes by themselves mean nothing. Only when the notes are arranged into musical sentences do they take on a definite meaning. Musical sentences are called PHRASES. Learn to think of your music *phrase by phrase.* Note how the little musical story above is told in TWO PHRASES.

5640

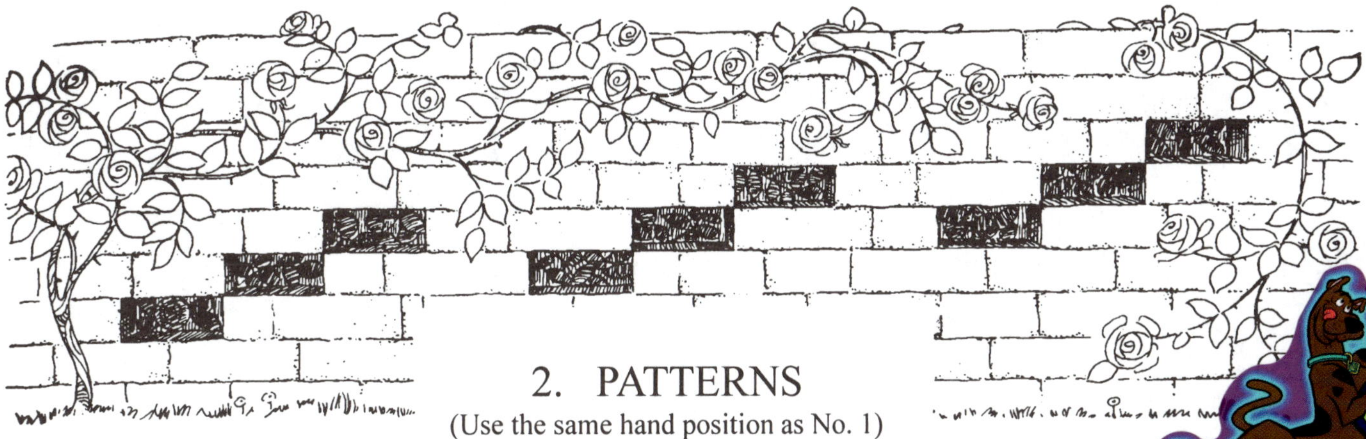

2. PATTERNS

(Use the same hand position as No. 1)

M.M. ♩ = 60 - 120

1st Phrase

Build-ers make their hous-es from a pat-tern that is neat.

2nd Phrase

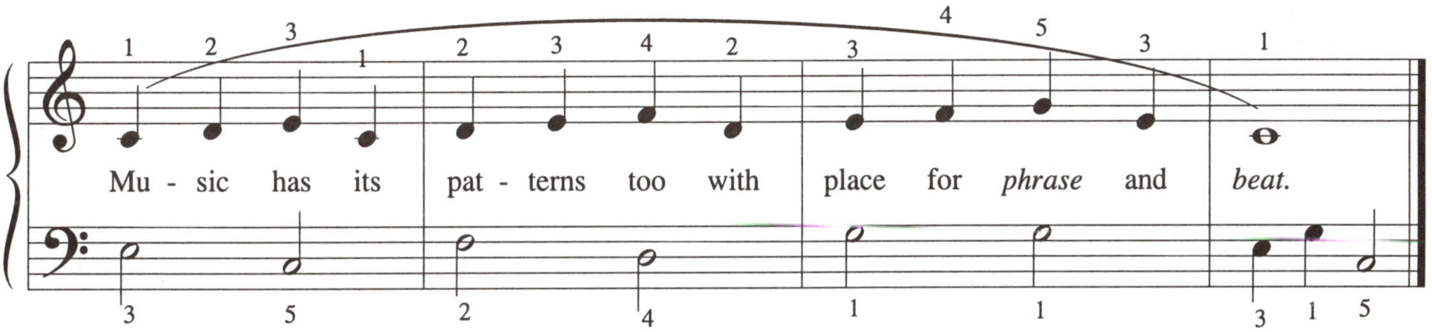

Mu-sic has its pat-terns too with place for *phrase* and *beat*.

MUSICAL FORM

Because it is built up of many well ordered PATTERNS, music has often been compared to architecture. We have in music *Melody Patterns, Rhythmical Patterns, Harmony Patterns* and (in piano music) *Finger Patterns*. The ability to recognize PATTERNS is very important. It makes for easier Sight-Reading, quicker Memorizing and more intelligent Interpretation.

THE MELODY PATTERN

Fix in your mind the above melody pattern in the right hand and note that the tones move THREE STEPS upward and ONE SKIP downward.

The same PATTERN one white key higher.

The same PATTERN another white key higher.

Note now that this design is repeated over and over throughout the little composition. Each design starts ONE TONE higher than the preceding pattern.

5640

Melody Pattern
One white key higher
Another white key higher

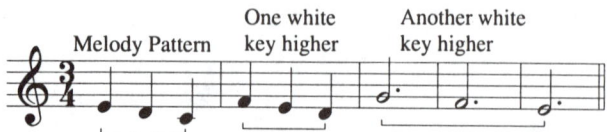

Practice C major hand position as in No. 1.

THE TIE

The TIE is a curved line joining one note to another of the SAME PITCH and means that the second note is to be held for its full value *without being struck.*

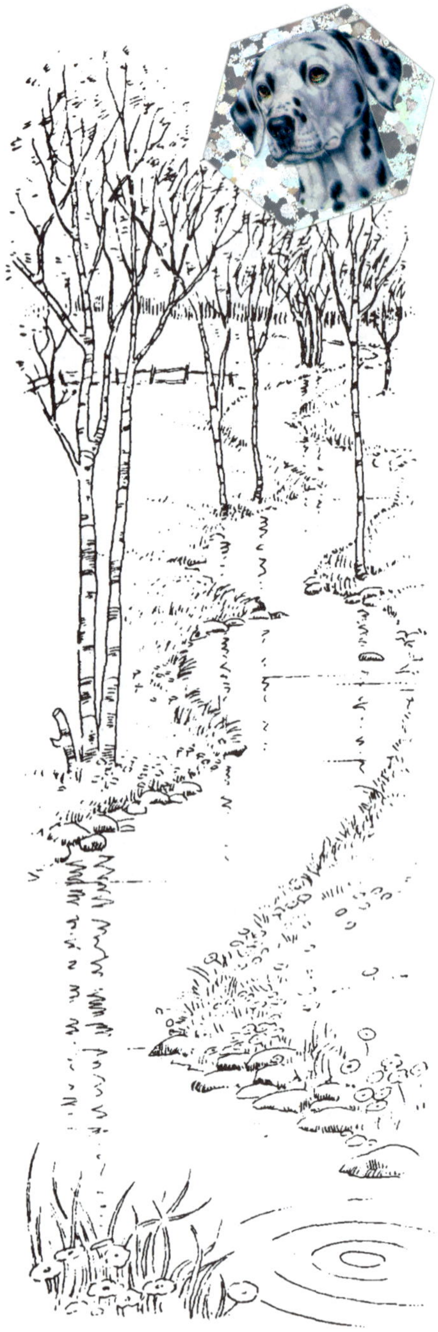

3. RUNAWAY RIVER

Moderato M.M. ♩ = 60 - 𝅗𝅥. = 50

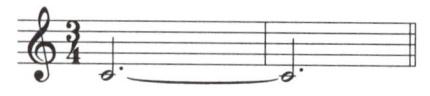

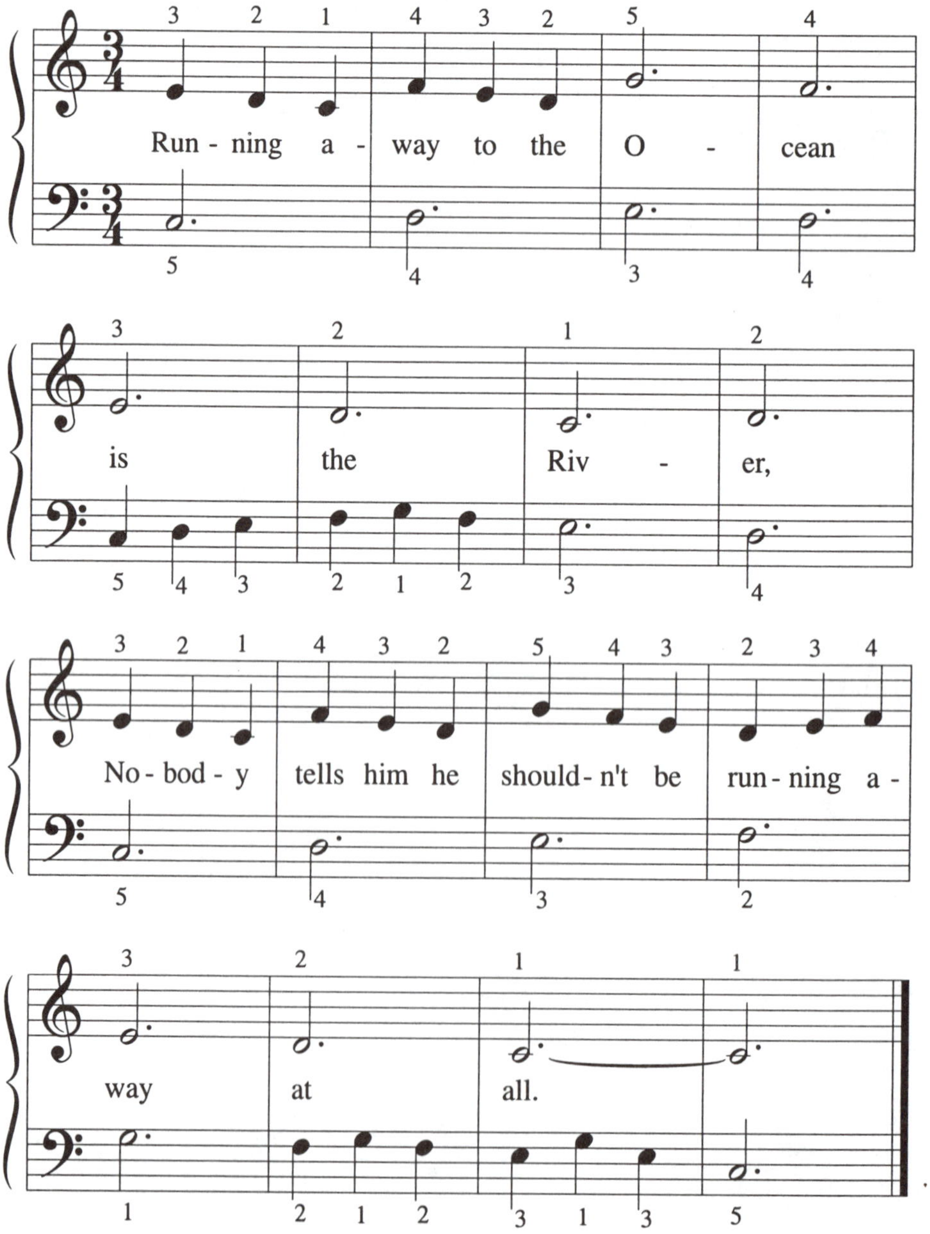
Run - ning a - way to the O - cean
is the Riv - er,
No - bod - y tells him he should - n't be run - ning a -
way at all.

RHYTHM and ACCENTS

RHYTHM has been called the *Soul of Music.* Rhythmical "swing" gives life to any composition. The first step in setting the RHYTHM is by means of the ACCENT. An ACCENT is a special emphasis placed upon ONE of the beats in a measure. RUNAWAY RIVER is written in THREE-FOUR time, which means ONE count to each quarter-note and THREE counts to each measure. *Always accent the first beat of each measure in three-four time.*

COUNT: | **ONE** two three | **ONE** two three | etc.

TWO-FOUR time signature means ONE count to each quarter-note and TWO counts to each measure. *Accent the FIRST note of each measure.*

COUNT: | ONE two | ONE two | etc.   Use the C major hand position.

Hunt for the MELODY PATTERNS.
Think of your pieces PHRASE by PHRASE.

4. THE TRAFFIC COP

TEMPO

TEMPO means TIME. A steady, even TEMPO is necessary to preserve the rhythmical swing. This means that there is no time to stop and hunt for notes or fingers. After a piece has been learned it should be reviewed until it can be played fluently and easily without stops or hesitation.

5640

TONAL SHADING:—As a painter creates beautiful pictures by lights and shadows, so do we add color to our musical pictures by means of TONAL SHADING. A MELODY LINE should constantly change in "thickness." This may be accomplished by adding MORE or LESS *intensity* to the tone. Everything possible should be done to make our music "flow." This applies equally to *Melody, Rhythm and Harmony.* "Contrast is the first law of all art."

THE MEANING OF THE EXPRESSION MARKS USED IN THIS PIECE

—Read Carefully—

(1) **MODERATO**—*At a moderate rate of speed or tempo.*
(2) **LEGATO**—*Bound together, play smoothly and connected.*
(3) *mf* = Mezzo-forte. *Half or moderately loud.*
(4) *p* = Piano. *Softly.*
(5) *f* = Forte. *Loud.*
(6) *pp* = Pianissimo. *Very Soft.*
(7) *mp* = Mezzo-piano. *Half or moderately soft.*
(8) **Rit.** = Ritard. *Gradual slowing up of tempo.*

5640

Half Steps

A HALF-STEP is the distance between any Key and the NEXT nearest Key to it.

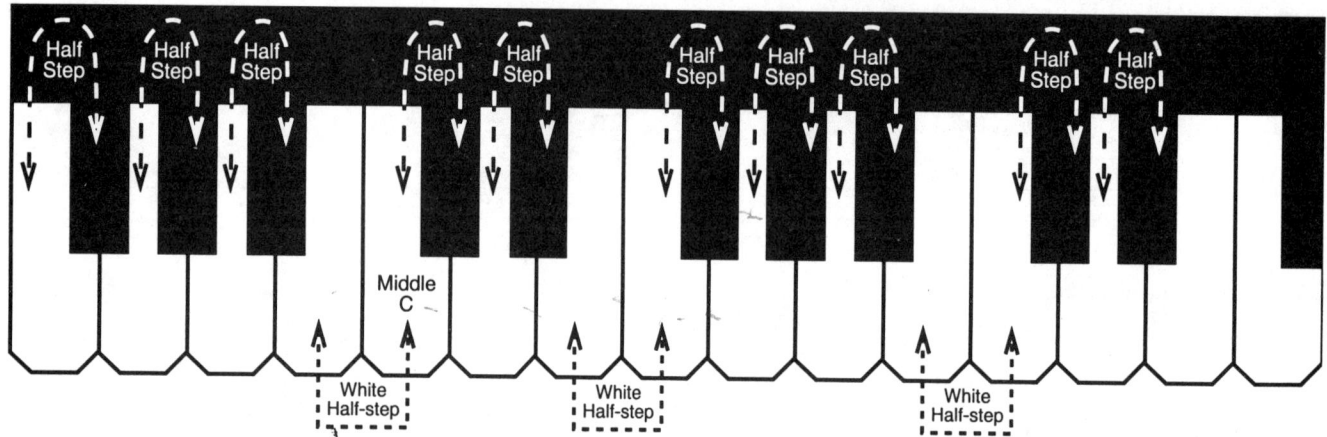

We find most of the HALF-STEPS are from a WHITE to a BLACK Key. There are, however, two WHITE HALF-STEPS--one between B and C and the other between E and F. Study them on this chart and locate them on the keyboard of your piano until they can be quickly recognized.

↑ # # # # # SHARPS AND FLATS ♭ ♭ ♭ ♭ ♭ ↓

A SHARP (#) placed before a note RAISES it a HALF-STEP

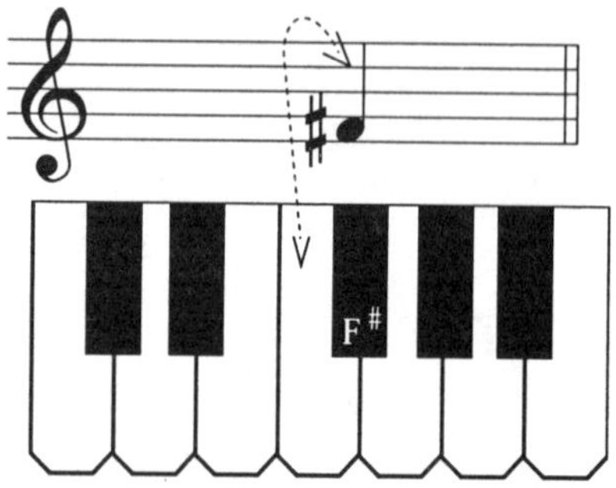

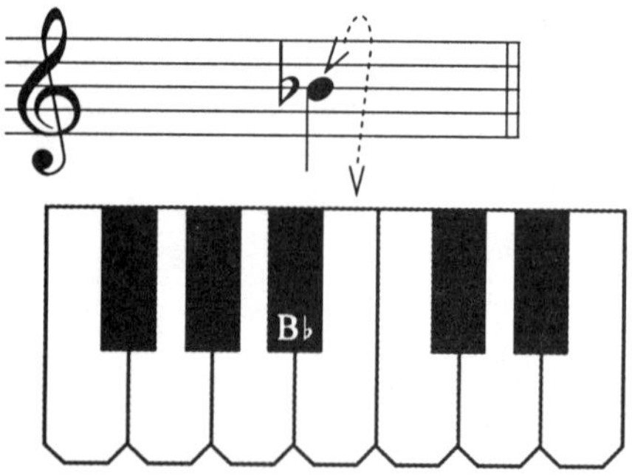

A FLAT (♭) placed before a note LOWERS it a HALF-STEP

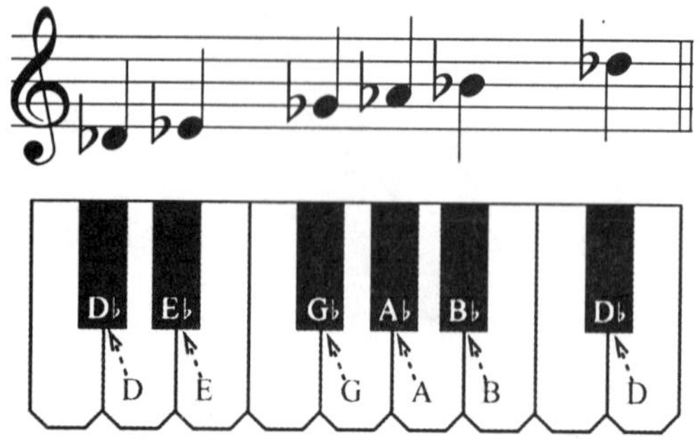

Always
Be
Careful to remember that

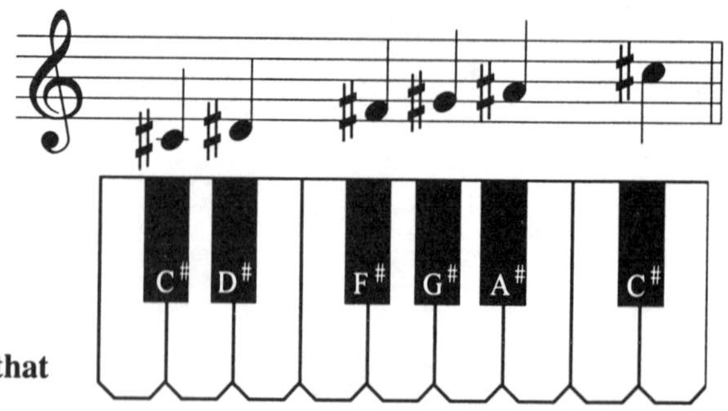

*A **BLACK** Key to the left of a white key is a FLAT (♭). A **BLACK** Key to the right of a white key is a SHARP (#).*

♮ ♮ ♮ NATURAL ♮ ♮ ♮

A NATURAL (♮) placed before a note which has been either SHARPED or FLATTED cancels the SHARP or FLAT.

5640

WHOLE STEPS

11

A WHOLE STEP is twice the distance of a half-step. Therefore, there will always be ONE KEY— either BLACK or WHITE— lying between.

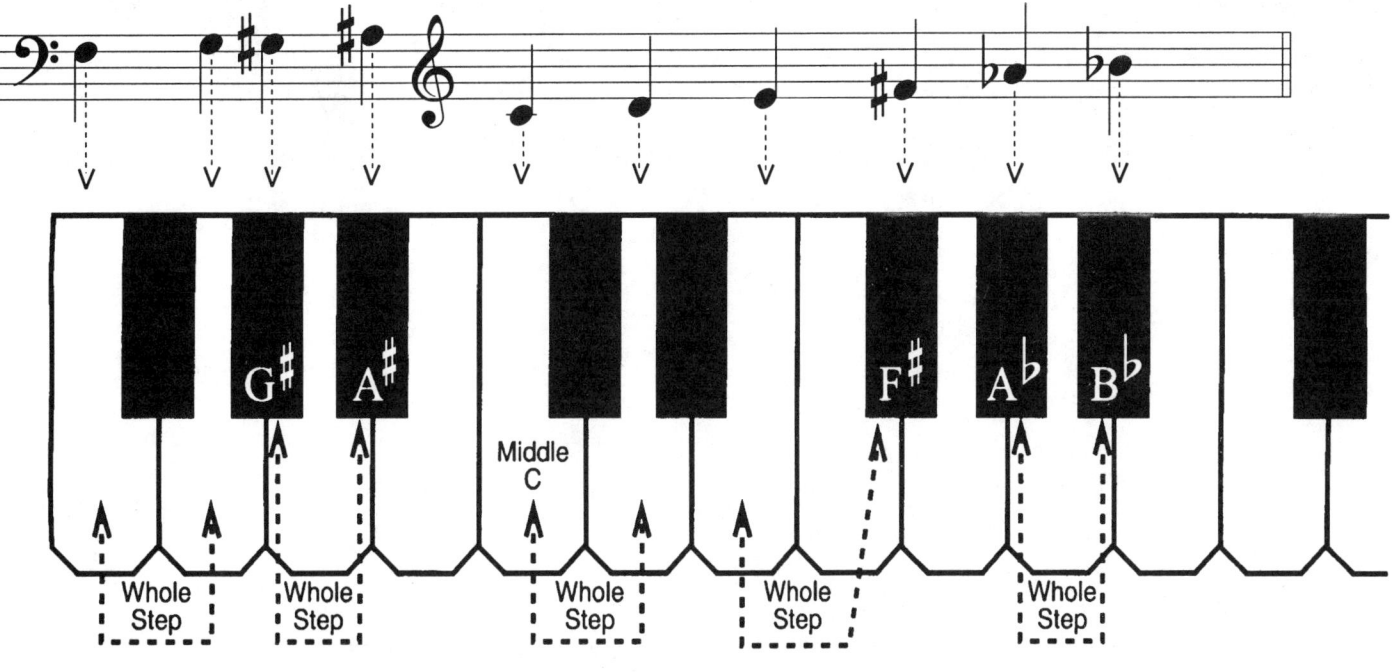

WHOLE STEPS AND HALF STEPS

Write the name of each STEP below the following examples.

From **F** to **G** is a **whole** step.

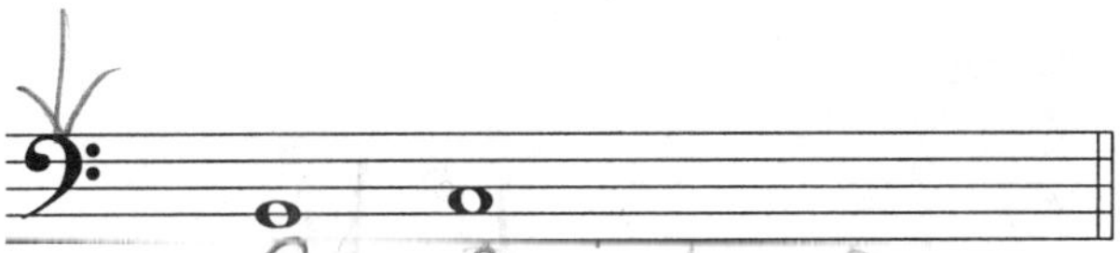

From **B** to **C** is a **half** step.

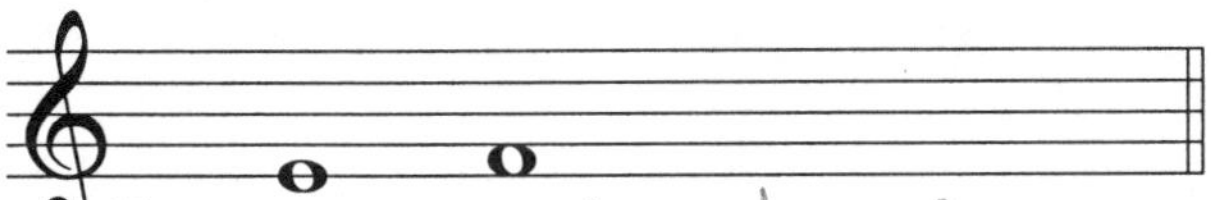

From **E** to **F** is a **half** step.

From **F** to **F#** is a **half** step.

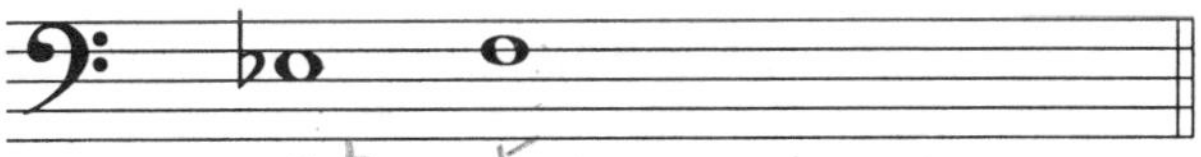

From **B♭** to **A** is a **half** step.

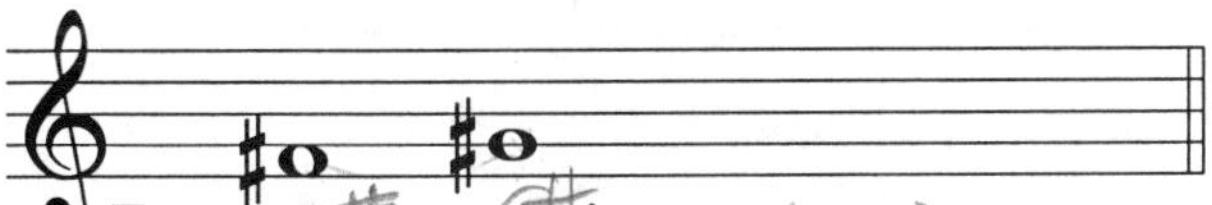

From **E♭** to **F** is a **whole** step.

From **F#** to **G#** is a **whole** step.

From **E♭** to **D♭** is a **whole** step.

5640

ACCIDENTALS

New hand position in C major
Shift the left hand three white keys upward to Middle C and practice each hand separately.

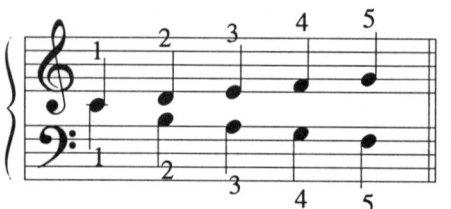

ALWAYS
BE
CAREFUL
to observe accidentals

The SHARP (♯) and FLAT (♭) signs used to raise or lower notes one HALF STEP are called ACCIDENTALS.

6 THE SCISSORS GRINDER

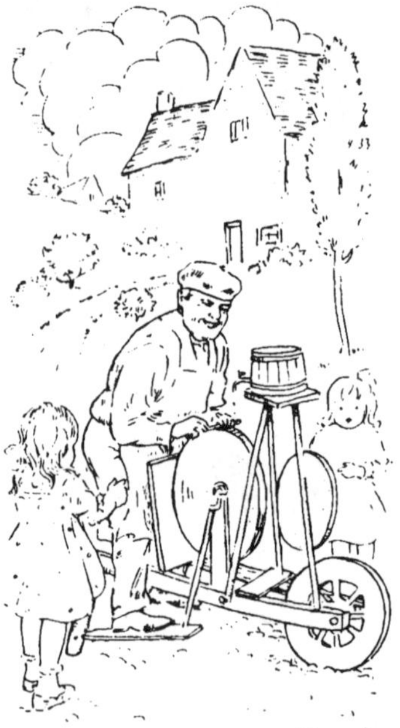

Moderato M.M. ♩ = 60 - ♩. = 54

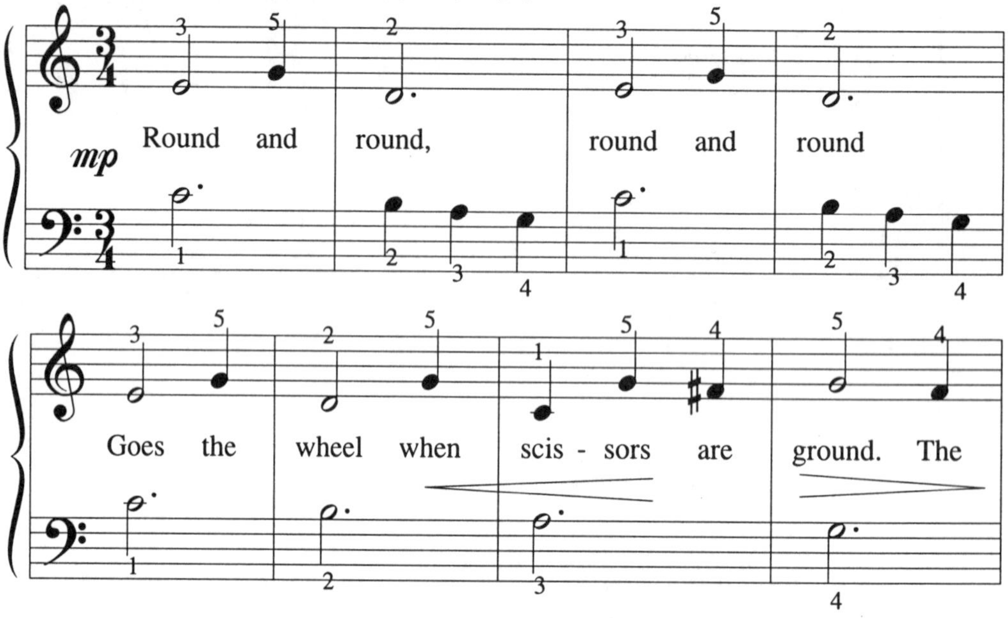

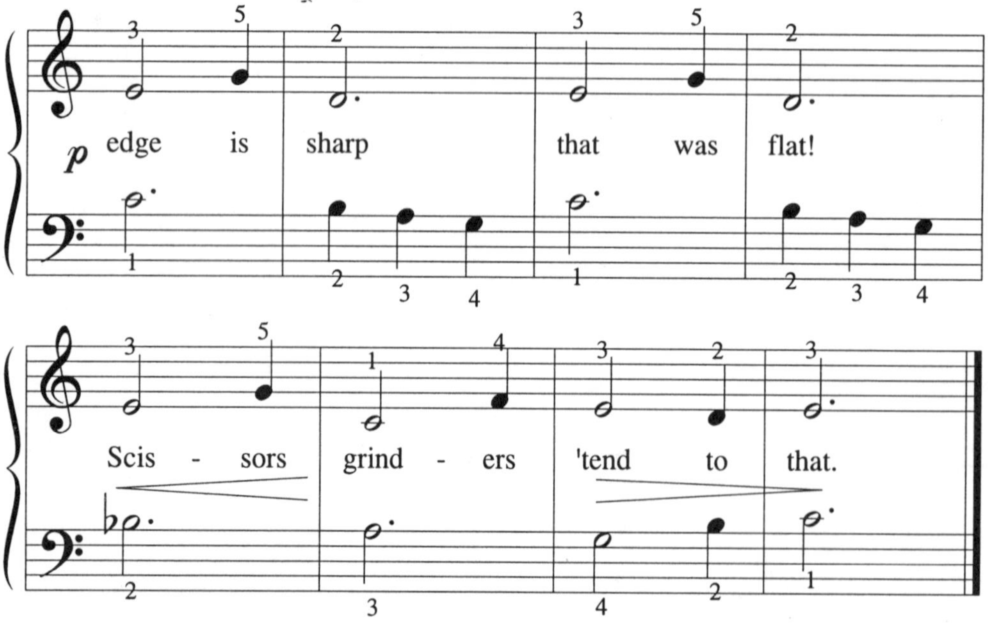

mp Round and round, round and round
Goes the wheel when scis - sors are ground. The
p edge is sharp that was flat!
Scis - sors grind - ers 'tend to that.

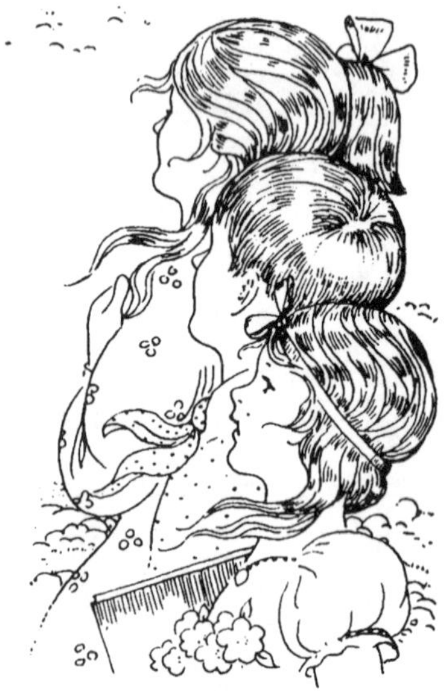

Play with as much expression as possible and note the new EXPRESSION SIGNS

⟨ means CRESCENDO, a gradual increase in tone.
⟩ means DECRESCENDO, a gradual decrease in tone.

NEW HAND POSITION

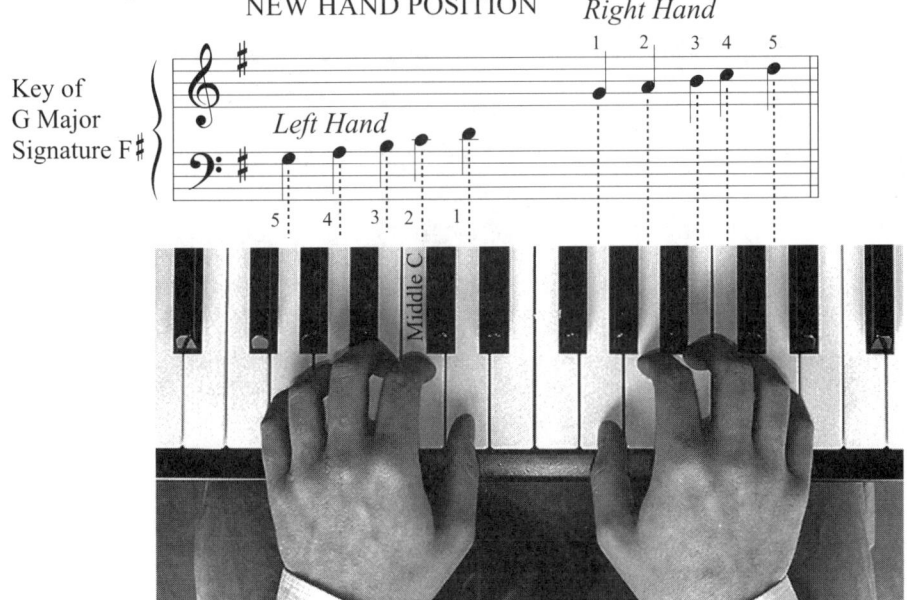

We change now to a new Key—*the Key of G major*—and consequently to a NEW hand position. Note the SHARP (♯) in the SIGNATURE. This means that all F's will be sharped (*played on a BLACK key*). Be sure to remember this. Place your hands in the NEW hand position and practice each hand separately before you play the piece.

7. A SONG OF PENNY CANDY

When un-cle Ben-ny gives me a pen-ny, I go trip-ping gai-ly to the lit-tle can-dy store.

Note to Teachers: *Students should be required to recite both Time Signature and Key Signature before playing each piece.*

NOTICE THE FORM of this little piece. The entire theme is written on two **MELODY PATTERNS.**

Andante means *moderately slow*

8. THE MAN IN THE MOON

Andante M.M. ♩ = 60 - ♩. = 54

Big Moon, Bright Moon;

Sail-ing so slow-ly high up in the star-ry sky;

Big Moon, Bright Moon;

rit.

Can you see peo-ple so lit-tle as I?

TRANSPOSITION: By means of FINGER PATTERNS the pupil should now be taught to transpose the C major pieces into the key of G major and vice versa. Simply find the five-finger position for the new key and play with the same fingers as in the original key. This idea should be carried on in each new key as learned.

FOLK TUNES. Some of our most beautiful melodies did not, as you might suppose, come from the pen of famous composers, but from the folk songs which originated among the common people. These melodies were not written down, but were passed along orally from generation to generation. Because of their charming simplicity, many of them will endure forever as masterpieces of melody. Note this beautiful old French folk tune which consists of two very short MELODY PATTERNS.

No. 1 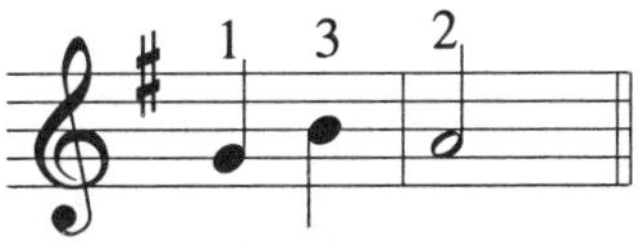   No. 2

9. THE PARTY

Old French Nursery Tune

Andante M.M. ♩ = 60 - 120

Count: Three four **ONE** two Three four

mp Come right in, Let's be-gin, We will have such fun to-day! Let's pre-tend Gyp's a friend, Come to gos-sip and to play, Dogs and *pp* toys, Songs and noise, These have made the hours— fly. "Bow-wow-wow," That is how Gyp is bid-ding us, "Good-bye."

rit.

MELODIES BEGINNING ON THE VARIOUS BEATS OF THE MEASURE

Melodies do not ALWAYS begin on the FIRST beat of the measure. This piece, for instance, begins *on the third beat,* adding an entirely new 'swing' to the rhythm. To produce this effect we must be careful to apply the ACCENT where it belongs—on the FIRST beat.

Count therefore: | Three four | **ONE,** two, THREE, four | **ONE,** two, THREE, four | etc.

5640

The Phrasing Attack

PHRASING in music is like BREATHING in speech—we take *short breaths* and *long breaths*. If we keep in mind to make our playing BREATHE AT THE END OF EACH PHRASE, it will strengthen the rhythm and add immensely to the interpretation.

In playing TWO-NOTE PHRASES, think of the words DROP-ROLL and the effect will come naturally. In the following example, play the *first* note with a gentle DROP of the arm and the *second* note with a ROLL of the arm and hand in an inward and upward motion, *using no finger action* and *releasing the note* on the upward roll.

The following illustration shows the proper position of hand and arm as each phrase is released. The WRIST must be completely relaxed.

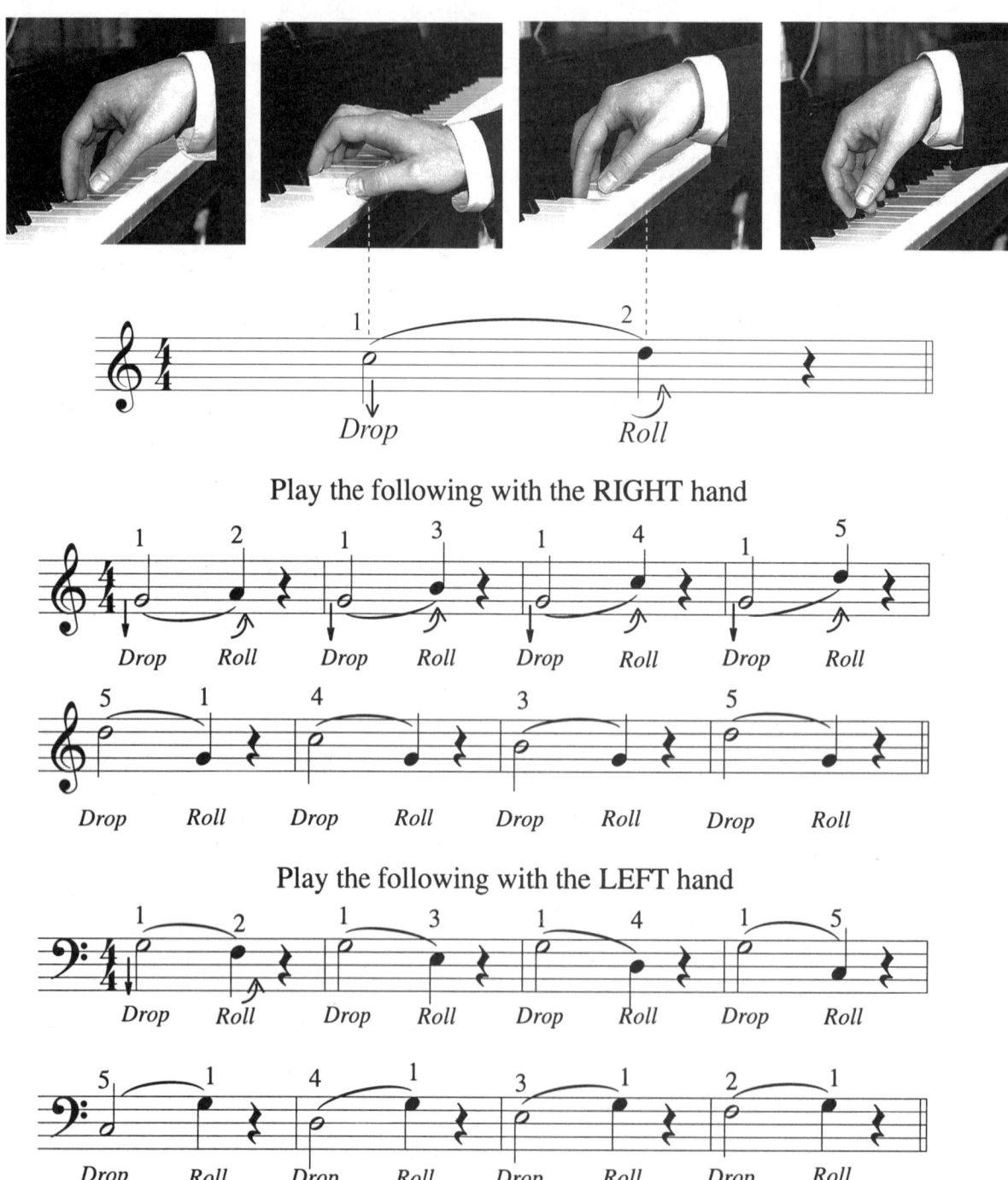

The SIGN of the phrase is the curved line, ⌒. All notes under this line, except the last one, should be played LEGATO. The last note must always be played with a rolling motion of the arm *forward* and *upward*.

At this stage of progress "The HANON Studies" by John Thompson should be assigned as supplementary work. This book is issued with attractive titles and illustrations, and is especially adapted for FIRST GRADE use to develop the PHRASING ATTACK as well as all the fundamental touches used in the pages of this book.

Combining HAND POSITIONS already learned

To play this piece we COMBINE the hand positions learned in Nos. 1 and 7. The right hand plays the FIVE-FINGER position beginning on C while the left hand plays the FIVE-FINGER position beginning on G.

Practice with the hands in this position then play "THE ROBIN."

10. THE ROBIN

Be sure to phrase the right hand as indicated by the curved lines using the DROP, ROLL attack.
COUNT: three | **ONE** two three | **ONE** two three | etc.

FINGER PATTERNS

Have you noticed how easy it is to transpose from ONE key to ANOTHER by means of the FIVE FINGER pattern? A knowledge of finger patterns is also very helpful when playing *beyond* the five-finger position.

Left hand

Drop Roll

In playing THE MERRY CLOWN, the left hand goes out of the five-finger position, but observe how easily the left hand trips DOWN the keyboard on a simple little "ONE-TWO" finger pattern.

Right hand

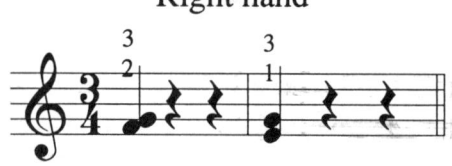

The right hand HARMONY pattern is also extremely simple, consisting of but TWO SMALL CHORDS.

Practice each PATTERN separately before playing hands together

11. THE MERRY CLOWN

M.M. ♩ = 80

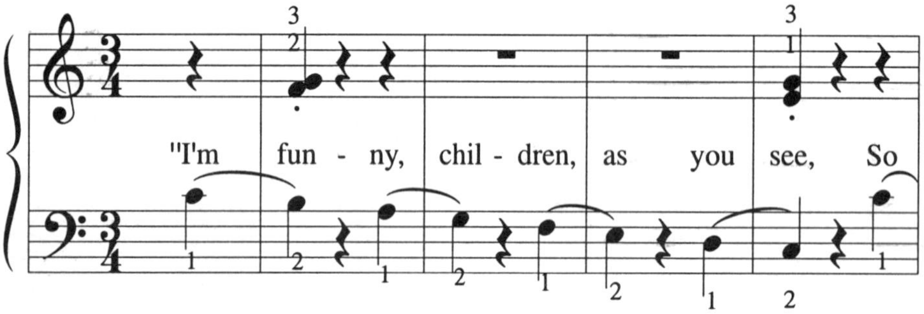

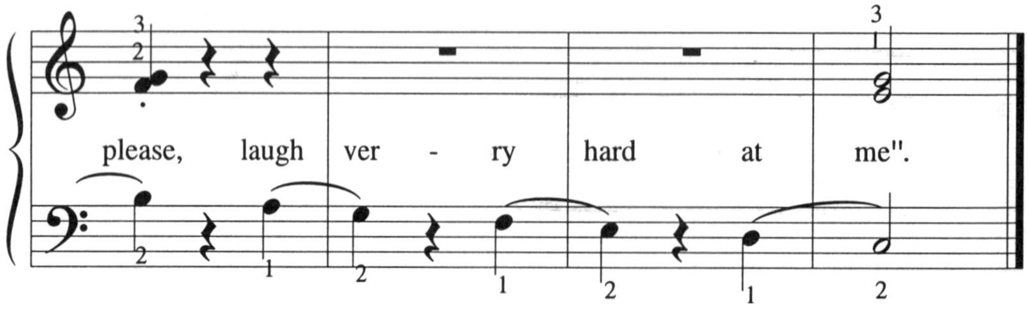

"I'm fun-ny, chil-dren, as you see, So please, laugh ver-ry hard at me".

Round dots (•) over or under notes indicate STACCATO—detached—short.

Be sure to observe the left hand phrasing by use of the DROP, ROLL attack.

**Always
Be
Careful** of the accent. The melody begins on the THIRD beat.

COUNT: three | **ONE** two three | **ONE** two three | etc.

5640

Nearly every phase of life in Germany is bound together in the national tie of folk songs—true songs of the people which reflect the moral, social and political life of the soldier, student, clerk and peasant. The early settlers in Pennsylvania and other states came to America singing these beautiful melodies while they worked. Later generations forgot the words of the "Vaterland" but not the tunes. College songs, patriotic songs, etc. have been adapted to them until many of them are now really a part of our own national life.

In "THE CUCKOO," both hands employ the PHRASING ATTACK. Place your hands in the G major five-finger position and be sure you are familiar with the HARMONY pattern in the left hand.

ff - fortissimo means very loud

12. THE CUCKOO
German Folk Tune

EXAMINATION No. 1

1. Explain the following TIME SIGNATURES and tell where the accents fall in each.

   $\frac{2}{4}$ $\frac{3}{4}$ $\frac{4}{4}$

   ....

   ....

2. What is a HALF-STEP? .... A WHOLE STEP? ....

3. Give the definition of the following:
   - **MODERATO** ....
   - **LEGATO** ....
   - **ANDANTE** ....
   - **RITARD** ....
   - **TEMPO** ....

4. Write the meaning and SIGNS of the following musical terms.
   - **FORTE** .... Its SIGN ....
   - **MEZZO FORTE** .... Its SIGN ....
   - **PIANO** .... Its SIGN ....
   - **MEZZO PIANO** .... Its SIGN ....
   - **PIANISSIMO** .... Its SIGN ....
   - **FORTISSIMO** .... Its SIGN ....

5. What are ACCIDENTALS and what effect do they have?

   ....

   ....

6. What are FOLK TUNES?

   ....

   ....

AVERAGE GRADE for examination No. 1

Attach Certificate No. 1 here

Note to teacher: *Students may be graded according to the preference of the individual teacher. Some teachers prefer the use of silver and gold stars; some grade by percentage, while others find the letter system of grading as used in schools more adaptable.*

When the above examination has been passed to the satisfaction of the teacher, the student should be awarded CERTIFICATE NO. 1 (See page 79 of this book) duly signed, dated and graded.

SCALES

The matter of Scales and Arpeggios practice is a much debated question among piano teachers. Some teachers begin scale work quite early in the student's career and are very insistent in the matter of daily practice. Others look upon them as a sort of unnecessary drudgery and claim that students can develop just as much facility in playing the scale and arpeggio passages that occur in the books and sheet music of their repertoire. Naturally, this resolves itself into a matter of individual judgement.

The author feels that since all music is made up of scales and arpeggio figures, or fragments thereof, pupils should be required to know something about them. All music has form and shape that should be recognized in order to aid interpretation and general musicianship. There is also a technical value to scale and arpeggio practice which cannot be summarily dismissed. Perhaps the real difficulty arises from the theory that most students look upon the scale as a dry, uninteresting exercise invented by the teacher as a special form of punishment. If more care were used in presenting the scale and a real effort made to have the student look upon the scale as a beautiful piece of musical architecture, the result would be quite different. As soon as the formation of a scale is learned, students should be assigned pieces in which the scale figure is employed as melody. In this way the student learns to greet the scale as an *interesting musical pattern* and one which will recur many times even in elementary repertoire.

There are many ways to teach the scales, but most of the variations are based upon two standard approaches. Some teachers prefer the *tetrachord* approach while others find the older formula (i.e., the half steps between the third and fourth and the seventh and eighth) more acceptable. Of course, this is a matter that will vary not only with teachers, but also with students. This book has been arranged so that either approach may be made at the discretion of the teacher.

The Finger Drills on pages 76-78 of this book contain exercises for the development of Scales and Arpeggios.

THE MAJOR SCALE

A SCALE is a succession of eight tones bearing letter names in alphabetical order, the last tone having the same letter name as the first. The figures 1, 2, 3, 4, 5, 6, 7, 8 are called the DEGREES of the scale.

A MAJOR SCALE is a succession of WHOLE steps and HALF steps.
The half steps occur between 3 and 4 and between 7 and 8 as follows:

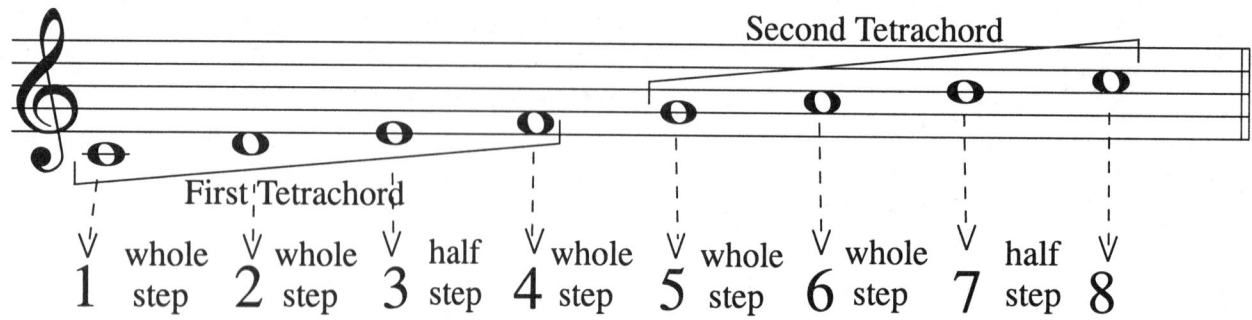

The above chart shows how a MAJOR SCALE is composed of TWO TETRACHORDS, each tetrachord *separated by a WHOLE step.*

Play the scale of C MAJOR as follows, using the fingers indicated.

SCALE OF G MAJOR

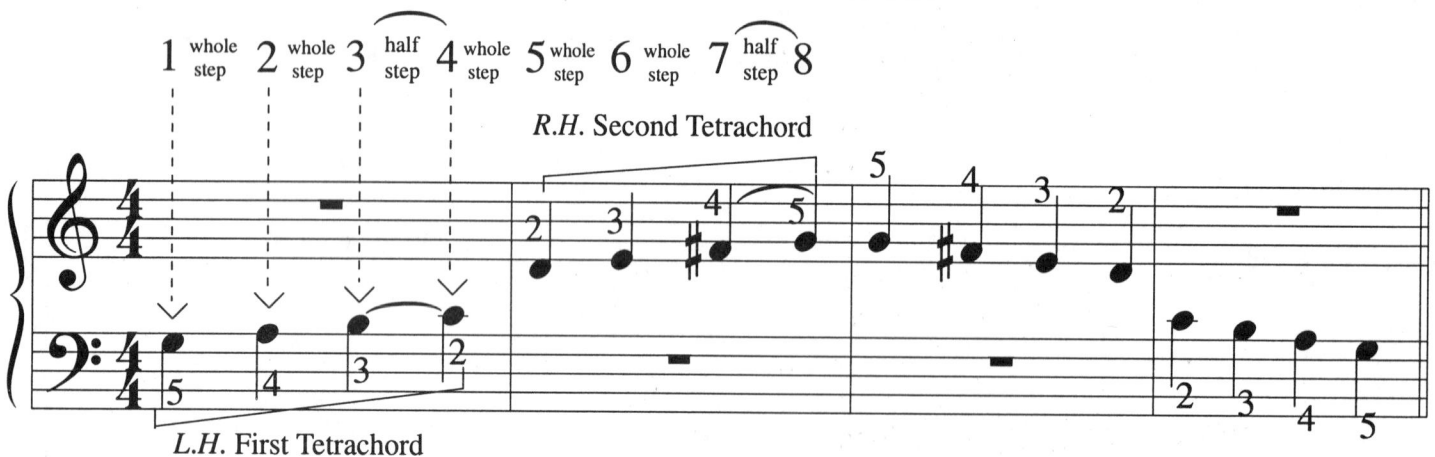

Note to Teachers: *During the progress in this book, it is advisable to adhere to the above form—the scale divided between the hands—until scale construction in all keys has been thoroughly mastered. This obviates the necessity of passing the thumb under and the hand over—a procedure which is comprehensively taken up and illustrated by examples in the SECOND GRADE book*

5640

SCALE OF C MAJOR—*Ascending*

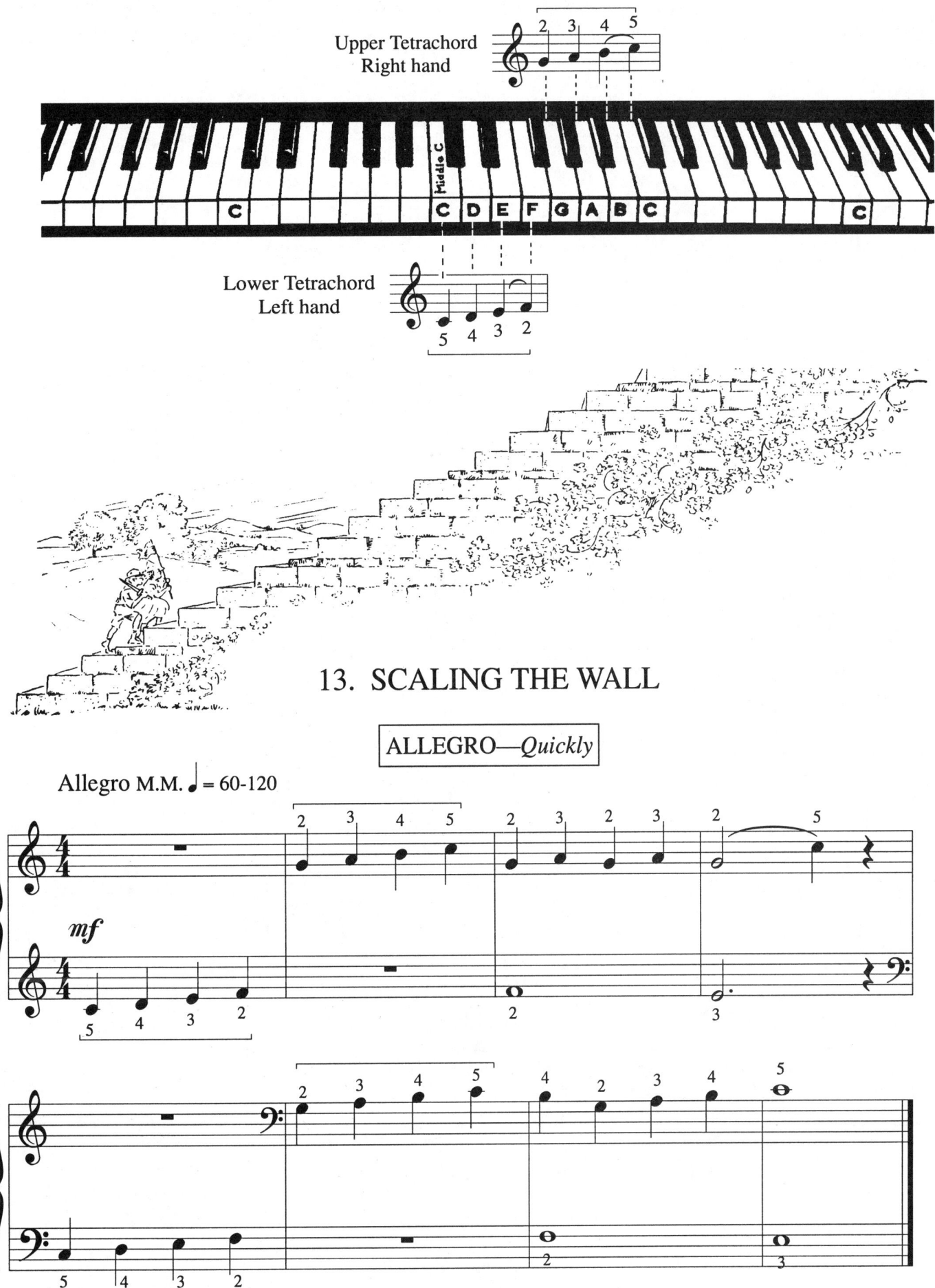

13. SCALING THE WALL

ALLEGRO—*Quickly*

Note to Teachers: *This is an excellent exercise for use in the various keys as they are learned. It should be played finally in all of the major keys.*

SCALE OF C MAJOR—*Descending*

14. THE CHIMES

Andante M.M. ♩ = 60-120

THE PEDAL

No doubt, your teacher has told you NOT to use the pedal. This has been done for an excellent reason, which you will appreciate when you have advanced a little further.

But perhaps as a reward for obedience in this matter, your teacher may, upon request, allow you to use the pedal just once in order to make THE CHIMES sound like real church chimes.

If permission is given, hold down the pedal from beginning to end. The result will be a blur which will be very unpleasant in most pieces—and that is one of the reasons your teacher does not want you to use the pedal yet. But in this particular tune it will give a clangorous muddle, typical of church chimes, filling the air with overtones.

15. STEPPING STONES

HALF STEPS: The melody in the right hand of STEPPING STONES passes through 16 half-steps of which 8 are *white key* HALF-STEPS. Can you locate all of them?

CHORD BUILDING
Intervals

An INTERVAL is the difference in pitch between 2 tones.

INTERVALS are measured by the number of LETTER NAMES contained between the LOWER and UPPER notes *inclusively*.

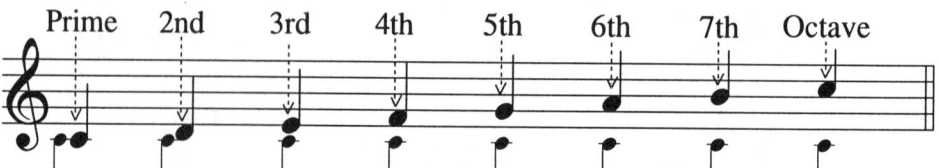

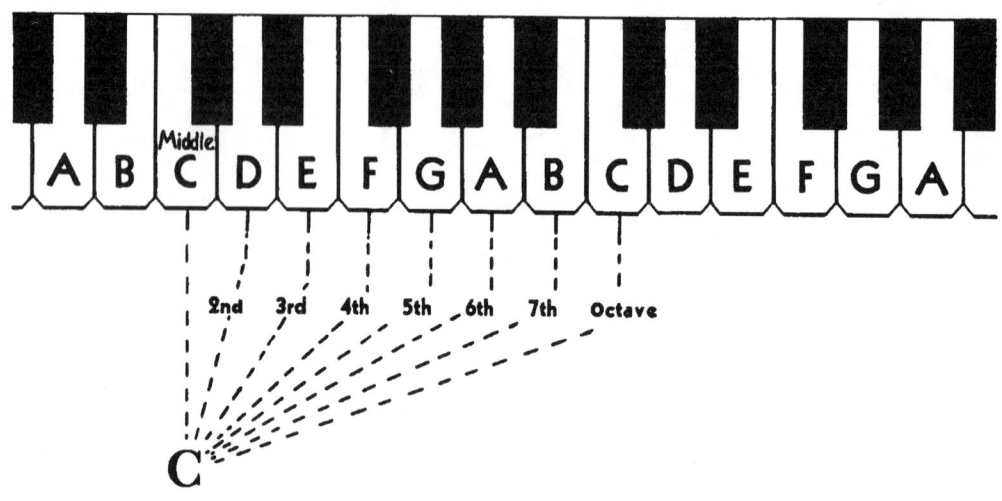

TRIADS

A CHORD is a group of THREE or more notes.

All SCALES are built in steps of 2nd's. For instance : *C to D, D to E; E-F etc.*
All CHORDS are built in steps of 3rd's. For instance : *C to E; E to G; G-B etc.*
The NOTE on which a CHORD is built is called the ROOT.

A TRIAD is a chord of THREE tones and contains a ROOT, a 3rd and a 5th.

EVERY CHORD IS NAMED FOR ITS ROOT

If we take the FIRST, THIRD and FIFTH notes of the Scale of C major 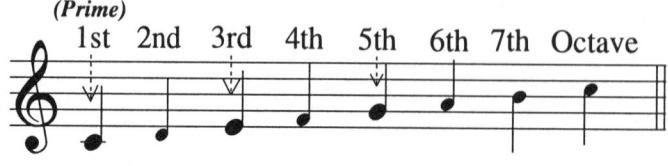 And sound them together thus:

we have played the **C MAJOR TRIAD**

G is the 5th
E is the 3rd
C is the ROOT

When the C major TRIAD or any CHORD is played in the following manner:

it is called a BROKEN CHORD or ARPEGGIO

(See Drills on pages 77-78 for Arpeggio practice)

5640

CHORD INVERSIONS

We have learned that a TRIAD contains a ROOT,
a 3rd and a 5th. The order of these tones may
change *without changing the name of the chord.*

When the lowest note is the ROOT, the triad is in the ROOT POSITION.

When the lowest note is NOT the ROOT, the triad is said to be INVERTED.

C MAJOR TRIAD

Example: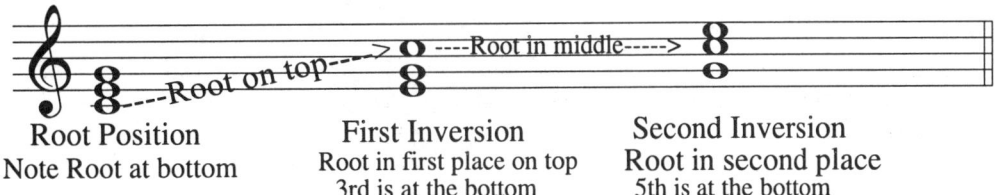

Root Position — Note Root at bottom

First Inversion — Root in first place on top, 3rd is at the bottom

Second Inversion — Root in second place, 5th is at the bottom

---

Simple rules for recognizing INVERTED CHORDS

TRIADS are in the ROOT POSITION when all the intervals of the Chord look alike; that is, when the notes are either ALL on the LINES or ALL in the SPACES.

Example: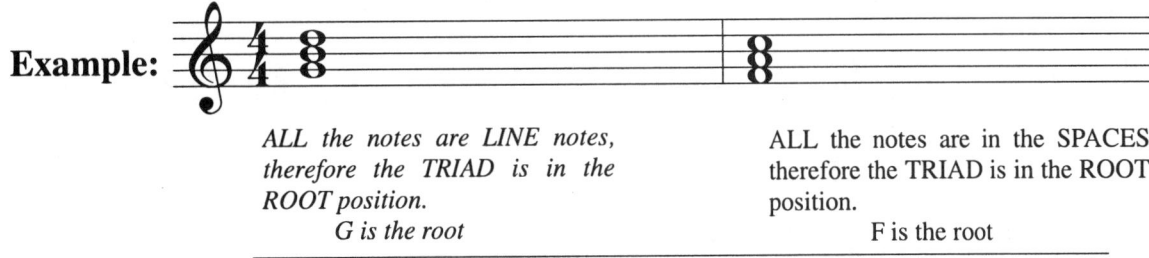

ALL the notes are LINE notes, therefore the TRIAD is in the ROOT position.
G is the root

ALL the notes are in the SPACES therefore the TRIAD is in the ROOT position.
F is the root

When TRIADS are INVERTED the intervals of the chord are unlike and appear mixed, that is, some of the notes are on the LINES and some are in SPACES.

C MAJOR TRIAD

Example: No. 1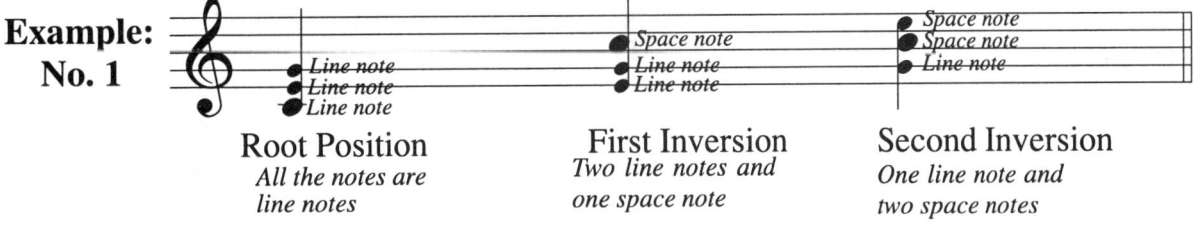

Root Position — *All the notes are line notes*

First Inversion — *Two line notes and one space note*

Second Inversion — *One line note and two space notes*

F MAJOR TRIAD

Example: No. 2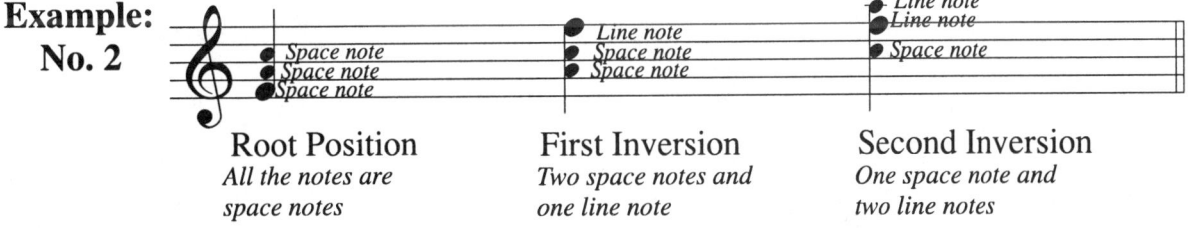

Root Position — *All the notes are space notes*

First Inversion — *Two space notes and one line note*

Second Inversion — *One space note and two line notes*

The ROOT is always the FIRST NOTE (counting upwards) to change its position from SPACE to LINE or from LINE to SPACE.

5640

C MAJOR HAND POSITION

In "MOUNTAIN CLIMBING" note how the BROKEN CHORD is used as melody. In the first two measures it is marked with a dotted circle. Locate the other broken chords and enclose each of them with a circle.

16. MOUNTAIN CLIMBING

Suggestions for supplementary solos in sheet form

FOREST DAWN in C major by John Thompson will prove an exemplary recital piece to facilitate BROKEN CHORD playing.

5640

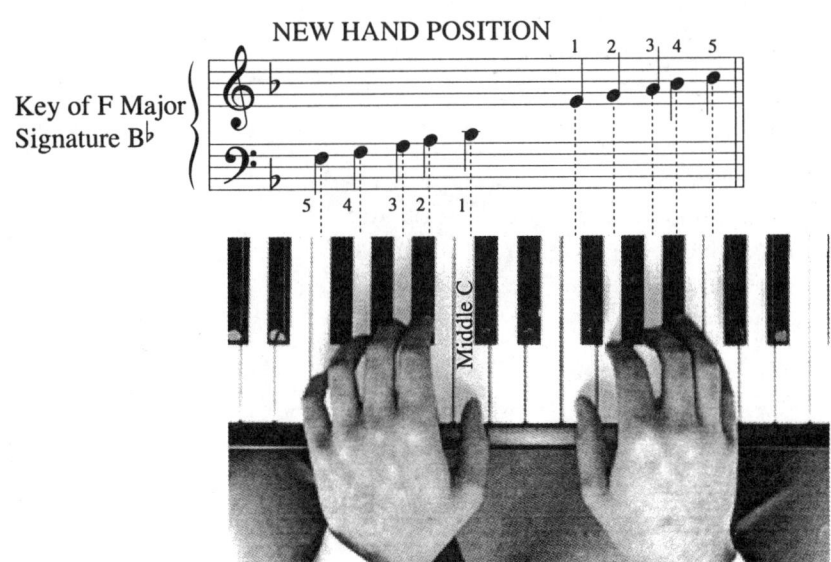

The **Key** of **F Major** has one **Flat** (♭) **B Flat.** Be sure to remember this while getting the "feel" of the keys in the new hand position and also when playing "A CHORD FROLIC."

Note how the BROKEN CHORD forms the melody. In the first measure it is marked with a dotted circle. Locate all other BROKEN CHORDS and enclose them with a circle.

17. A CHORD FROLIC

FIRST RECITAL PIECE

Here is your first real recital piece! See if you can learn it well enough to play on the next program presented by your teacher. Remember all the points you have learned thus far about *rhythm, tone coloring, expression, broken chords, etc.,* and apply your knowledge to this little piano solo.

A WAVY LINE preceding a chord means that the notes of the chord are to be BROKEN instead of sounded together.

18. THE FAIRIES' HARP

A fairy harp hangs in the wood
Played by every breeze,
Vanished today are the fairy folk
Who hung it high in the trees.

A FIRST INTRODUCTION TO EIGHTH-NOTES

Note to Teachers: *Frequently, we hear differences of opinion over the question of allowing students to say "and" when counting eighth-notes. As with all other controversial subjects in music, it is ridiculous to say that "This and this only is the correct way to teach." The progressive teacher applies his or her own individuality to the respective characteristic of each student. Whatever may prove successful with one may fail utterly with another. Experiment with ALL the approaches you know and use the one which justifies itself. It is often easier for a student to grasp the idea that there are TWO EIGHTH NOTES to ONE COUNT rather than "an eighth note gets HALF a count." Small children know nothing about fractions. Perhaps the simplest way is to play a few EIGHTH notes for the student and allow the EAR to catch the rhythmical inflexion rather than try to appeal to the student's mathematical faculties at this stage.*

TWO HAND POSITIONS IN THE KEY OF C MAJOR

You have learned to change from one hand position to another in playing different pieces. Now it is necessary to make a change of position *in the same piece*. It will not be difficult, however. You have played in both positions before and you have plenty of time in which to make the shift.

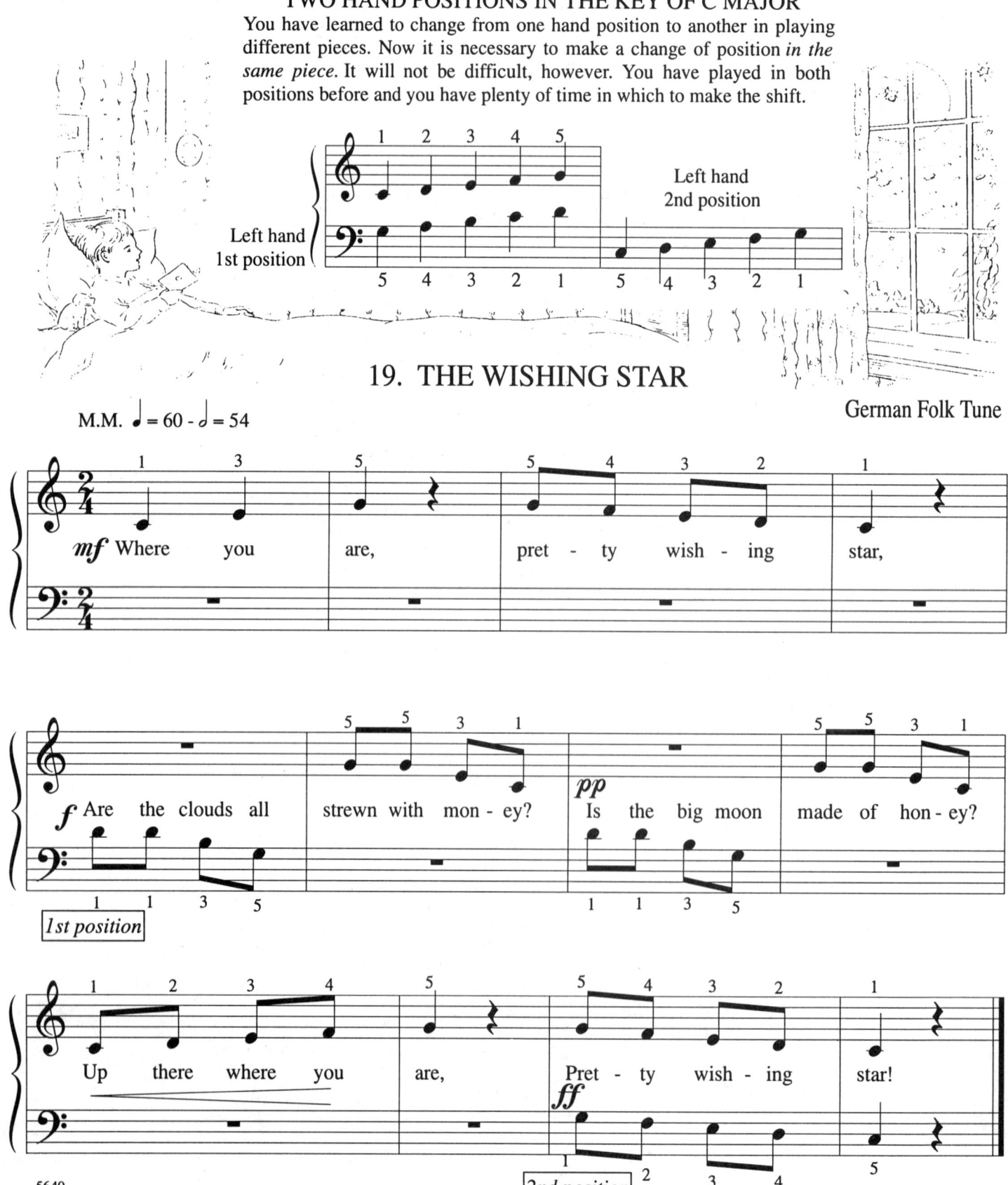

19. THE WISHING STAR

German Folk Tune

20. LIGHTLY ROW

Key of D Major Signature F♯ C♯

NEW HAND POSITION

See how nicely you can phrase "LIGHTLY ROW" by using the DROP and ROLL attack on the two-note phrases. On the extended phrases DROP on the first note, connect all notes in between, and ROLL off on the last note.

Moderato

Light - ly row! light - ly row! O'er the glass - y waves we go;

Smooth - ly glide! smooth - ly glide! On the si - lent tide.

Let the winds and wa - ters be Min - gled with our mel - o - dy;

Sing and float! sing and float! In our lit - tle boat.

5640

NEW HAND POSITION
with one note extension

Key of A Major Signature F♯ C♯ G♯

One note extension in left hand

Middle C

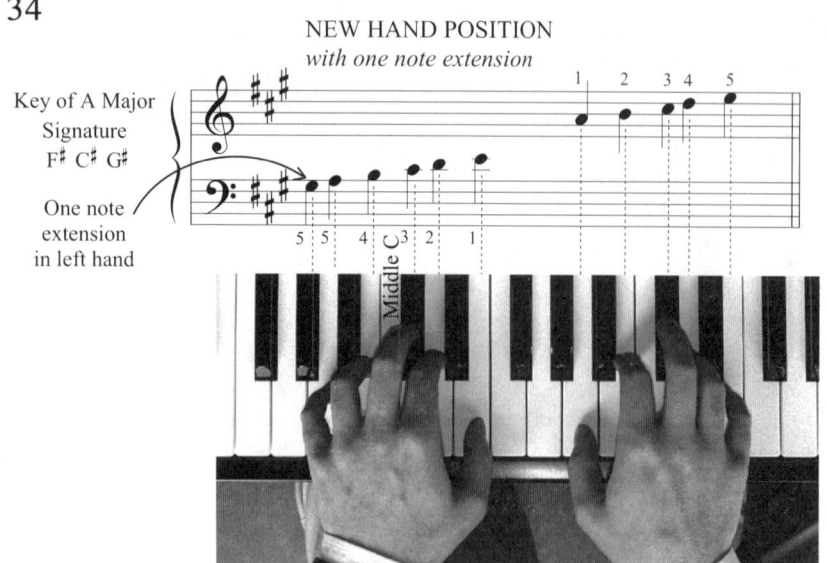

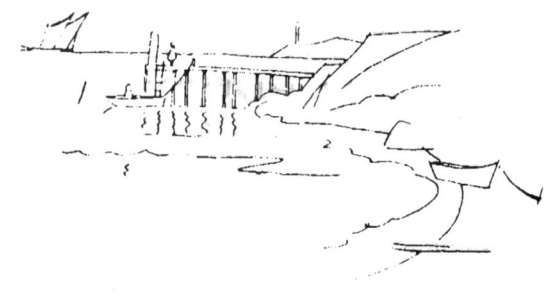

The KEY of A MAJOR has THREE SHARPS—F#, C# and G#.
Here again we have a recital piece. This calls for a smooth and beautiful singing tone.

21. LITTLE SPRING SONG

Andantino M.M. ♩ = 60 - 𝅗𝅥. = 50

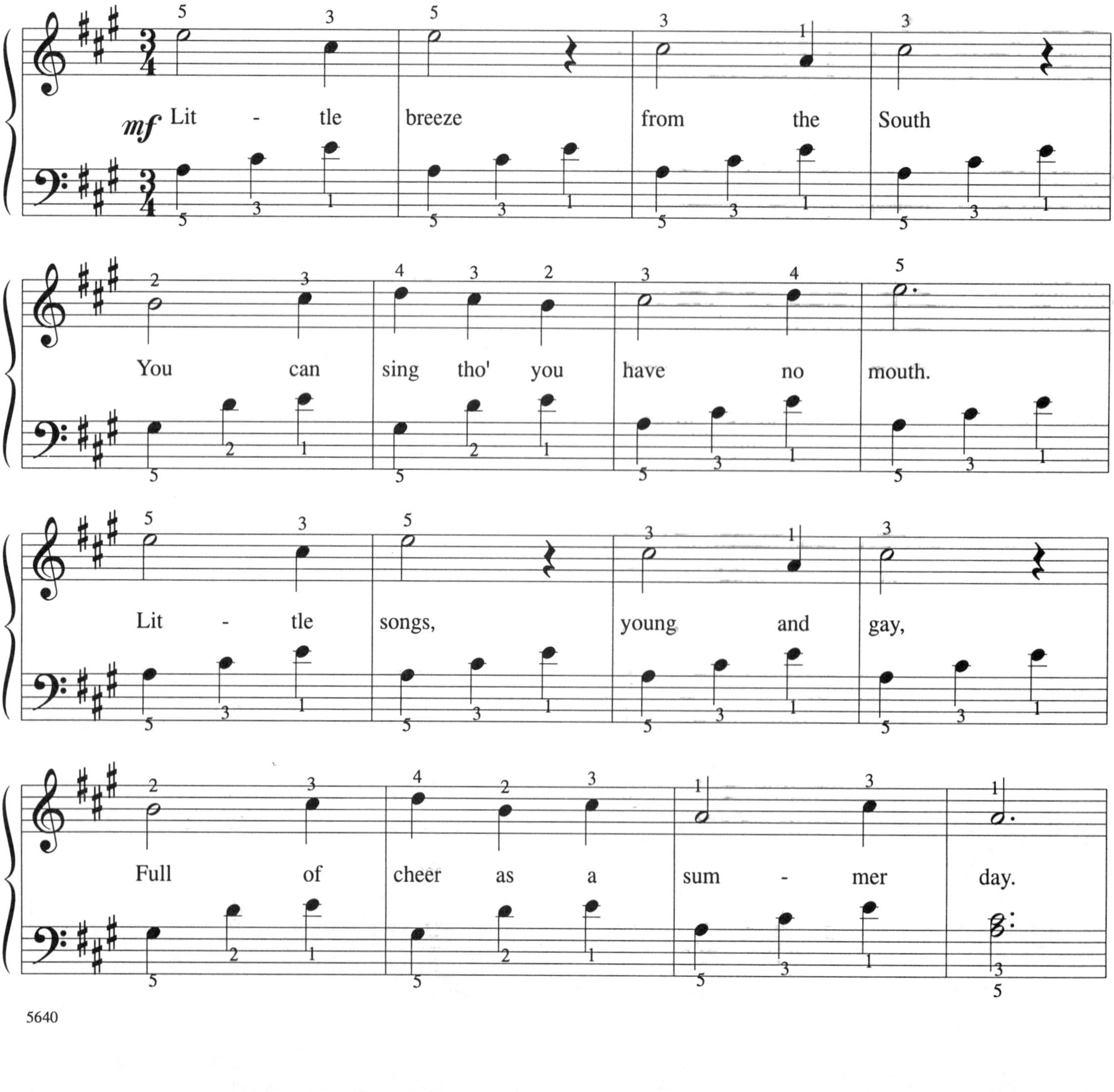

mf
Little breeze from the South
You can sing tho' you have no mouth.
Little songs, young and gay,
Full of cheer as a summer day.

Lyrics under the music:

All the birds and the beast-ies too, Seem to know that the win-ter's through! And the grass, as you pass, Whis-pers low "It is Spring, Sweet Spring."

r.h. over

pp

rit.

Suggestions for supplementary solos in sheet form:

TSCHAIKOWSKY: "Marche Slave"; BRAHMS: "A Lullaby"; two FIRST GRADE solos especially arranged by John Thompson to follow the above example showing the masters' use of the scale as a melody.

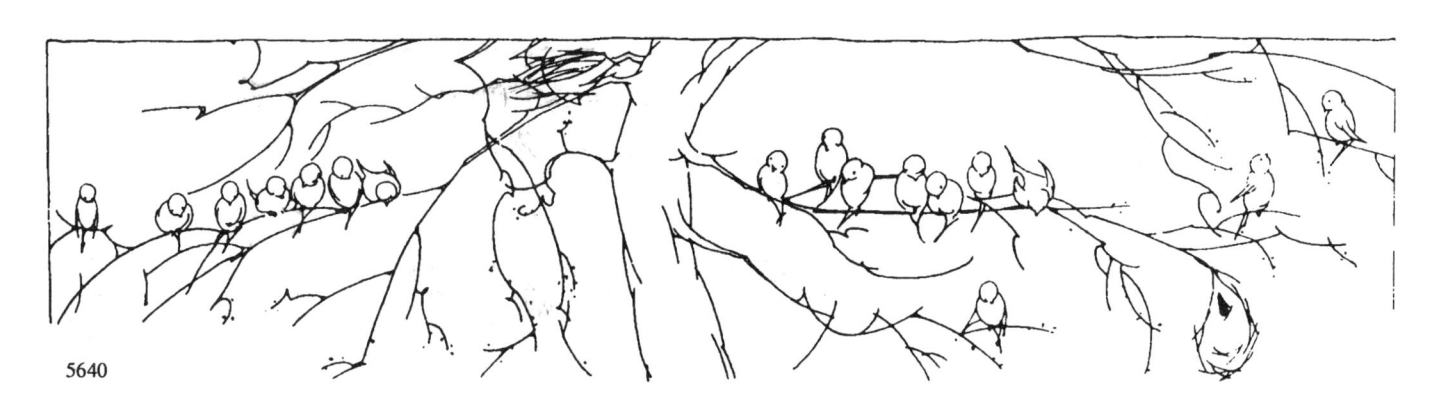

Make as much contrast as possible between the STACCATO notes and the LEGATO groups in this piece. Also see how much tonal shading you can put into it. Note the decided shading from *ff* to *pp* in the last line.

Lay special emphasis on the notes marked with the accent sign thus,

22. FALLING LEAVES

Dry leaves float down with every gust
Because old Autumn says they must!

DANCE FORMS

In music, RHYTHM is always uppermost. This is particularly true when playing *Dance Forms*. It is the rhythm that gives the dance its distinctive character. In a Dutch Dance the accent is a very heavy one. The first beat is usually phrased into the second and tossed off sharply. Imagine Dutch children dancing in their wooden shoes and see if you can make this piece suggest the land of canals, dykes and tulips.

23. DUTCH DANCE

Lyrics:
Dance for us, Sing for us, Gretchen and Hans! Click, click, go the wooden sabots and on goes the dance! Oh, we could stay here and watch you 'til the day is ended; Our dear little Gretchen and funny little Hans.

A Descriptive Recital Piece

This recital piece can be easily learned if studied in the following manner:

First: Analyze the INTRODUCTION which consists of the F major chord, built up *note by note* as each new trumpeter joins the Fanfare.

Next: Examine the left hand HARMONY PATTERN which is very simple, consisting of only two chords.

Practice them in this manner until you can make the shift easily.

Play the left hand chords with Wrist Staccato, using a snappy, bouncing wrist. Next apply the right hand making a nice contrast between staccato and legato. Keep the Tempo in strict March Time and play with military precision. Note the F major scale divided between the hands in measure eleven.

24. THE FAIRY COURT

⌢ = Pause - Hold

M.M. ♩ = 96

Salute to the Fairy Queen

In strict March Time

The Royal Procession

The Queen ascends the Throne

EXAMINATION No. 2

1. Of what is the MAJOR SCALE composed? ....

2. What degrees of the scale are used in building the MAJOR TRIAD?
   ....

3. What are INVERSIONS? ....
   How many INVERSIONS has the TRIAD? ....

4. What is the value of an EIGHTH NOTE? ....
   Grade on above ORAL examination ....

5. Play the following SCALES, first reciting the KEY SIGNATURE of each.

   Grade

   C major   ....
   G major   ....
   F major   ....
   D major   ....
   A major   ....   *Average grade for SCALE playing*..............

6. Play the following TRIADS in ROOT position, 1st INVERSION and 2nd INVERSION, naming each position.

   Grade

   C major   ....
   G major   ....   *Average grade for TRIAD playing*..............
   F major   ....
   D major   ....
   A major   ....

AVERAGE GRADE
for examination No. 2

....

Attach Certificate No. 2 here

5640

Play this number with a "pecking" sort of wrist staccato. The wrist should bounce freely and easily, but at the same time crisply.

25. THE TIRESOME WOODPECKER

The Woodpecker is a bird
That makes me exceedingly tired!
To go tapping like that for my food
I simply couldn't be hired!

Moderato

Note to Teachers: *For further development of WRIST STACCATO use "The HANON Studies" by John Thompson, page 10.*

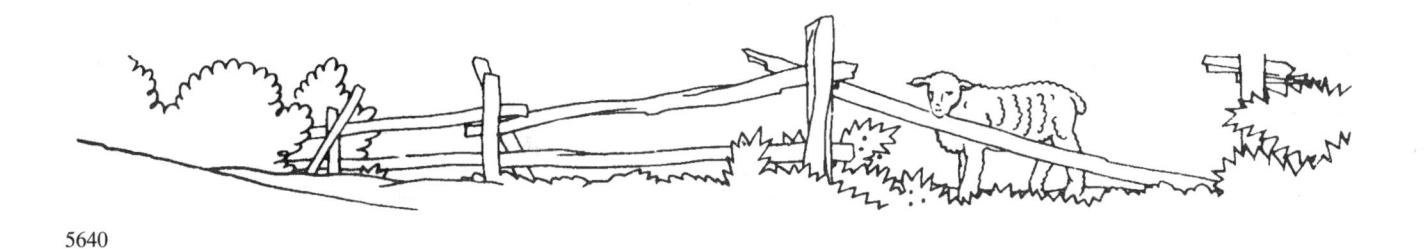

Practice the left hand HARMONY PATTERN before beginning the piece:

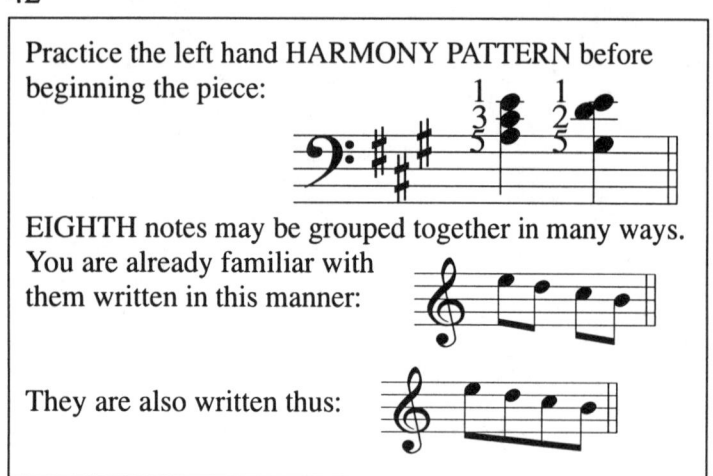

EIGHTH notes may be grouped together in many ways. You are already familiar with them written in this manner:

They are also written thus:

Extended hand position for the Left hand

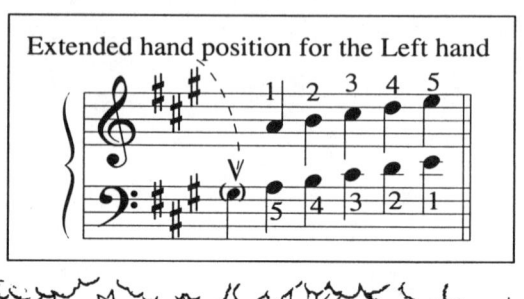

25. THE KNIGHT AND THE LADY

Riding through the green and leafy wood
Comes a lady wearing cloak and hood,
She is very sad,
Isn't that too bad?
Surely we would help her if we could!

Lo! a gallant knight comes riding by,
How he hates to see a lady cry!
He will take her part,
Win her gentle heart,
Quietly we'll leave them, you and I.

DOTTED QUARTER NOTES

You have already played *dotted half-notes* and learned how the DOT set after a note increases the time of that note by half its value. Therefore, if a QUARTER-NOTE is equal to ONE count, a dotted quarter-note will naturally be equal to ONE COUNT and A HALF,— or one full beat and half of the next one.

Introduction of the *dotted quarter-note* adds a new RHYTHMICAL PATTERN to those already learned.

NEW HAND-POSITION

Practice EACH HAND SEPARATELY

By reciting the word "Cumberland" you will get the "feel" of the *dotted quarter*. Before playing this piece practice this exercise and the NEW HAND POSTION.

CUM - ber - land, CUM - ber - land, CUM - ber - land.

27. "AIR" from MOZART

M.M. ♩ = 138

Mozart, as a boy

Mozart was the most musical boy that ever lived. He was born in the little town of Salzburg, in Austria, Jan. 27, 1756.

When the boy was four his father gave him his first music lesson; when he was 6 years old he composed a little minuet and while still a child played at court for King Francis I and Queen Maria Theresa of Austria.

5640

28. A LITTLE WALTZ

Moderato M.M. ♩ = 60 - 108

This piece follows almost the exact rhythmical pattern used by Brahms in one of his most famous waltzes.

NEW HAND POSITION

Key of B♭ Major Signature B♭ E♭

A NOCTURNE is a Night Song. It is a composition written in lyric style suggesting the peace of evening.

This one is written in the key of Bb major. The melody in the right hand should be played with a smooth *singing tone*. Make the phrases "breathe" on the 2nd and 4th lines. Play the left hand with a light touch so that the *singing tone* will predominate in the right hand.

29. THE OWL'S QUESTION
(Nocturne)

Andante M.M. ♩ = 60 - 𝅗𝅥 = 58

mp When be - neath the oaks I prowl,

"Who - oo?" "Who - oo?" asks the owl,

Pleas - ant - ly I call my name,

He cries "Who - oo?" just the same.

5640

SIX-EIGHT TIME

> In six-eight time there are SIX counts to the measure and *an eighth note gets one count*. There are TWO accents to the measure, the primary accent falling on the FIRST count and a secondary accent on the FOURTH count.
>
> A dotted quarter-note, of course gets THREE counts in *six-eight time*.

Note to Teachers: *When students can play these six-eight examples up to tempo they should be taught to count* two *to the meausre.*

30. CHEER FOR THE BLUE

Allegretto M.M. ♩. = 60-80

Brek- ek - ek, Brek- ek - ek, Brek- ek - ek - ek, Ray! Par - a - ba - loo!

Brek - ek - ek, Brek- ek - ek, Brek- ek - ek - ek, Yea, cheer for the blue!

The RHYTHM in the CUCKOO CLOCK begins on the SIXTH count.

Always
Be
Careful, therefore, to count as follows:
six | **ONE,** two, three, Four, five, six | etc.
Be sure to observe the TWO-NOTE phrases of the right hand, using the DROP and ROLL (Phrasing) attack.

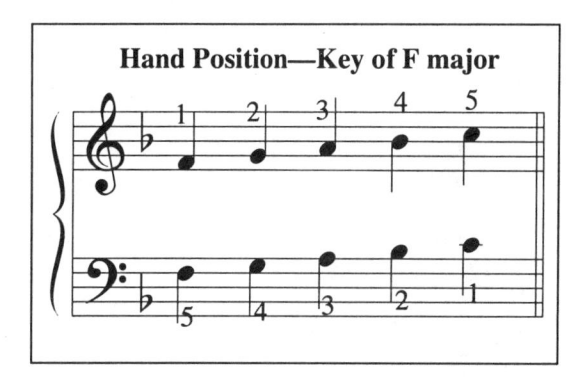

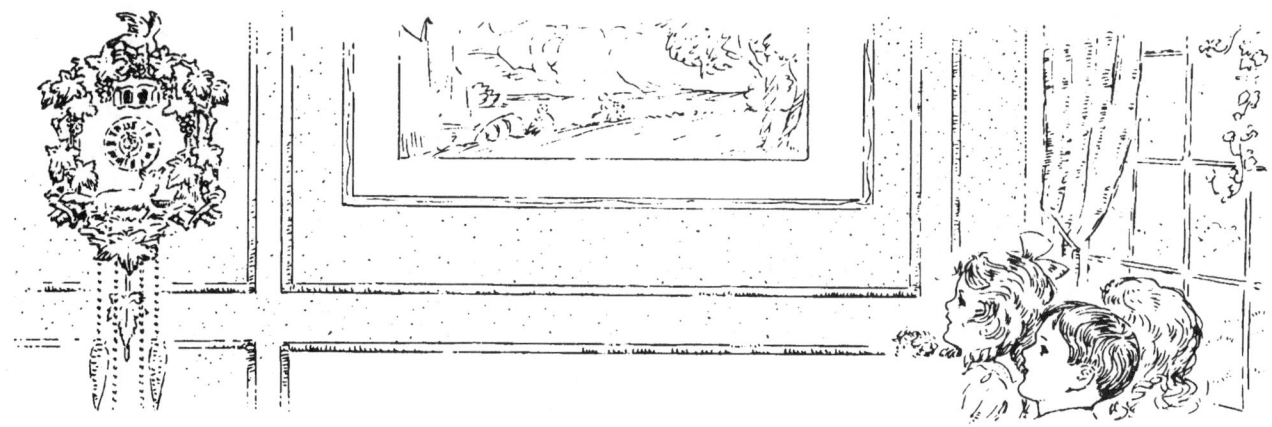

Hand Position—Key of F major

31. THE CUCKOO CLOCK

Hand Position—Key of G major

32. THE SINGING MOUSE

I'm not an ordinary mouse,
I lend distinction to a house!
Who wouldn't like to see
A singing mouse like me?

M.M. ♩. = 60 - 80

33. THE BIRTHDAY CAKE

No wonder the children to whom I come
Greet me with shouts and cheers,
I'm the glowing and beautiful Birthday Cake
That marks the passing years.

M.M. ♩. = 60 - 120

D. S. (Dal Segno) al fine means go back to the sign (𝄋) and play to Fine.

PLAYING IN TWO POSITIONS

In this piece we shall play in TWO "HAND POSITIONS."

Practice the positions separately by changing from one position to the other and back again before attempting to play "The POPCORN MAN."

OBSERVE the STACCATO notes. It is suggested that the *wrist staccato* be used.

First Position

Second Position

34. THE POPCORN MAN

1st position Pop-corn Man Mis-ter Pop-corn Man, What a heap you've got in that white pan! O if I were rich as I'd like to be, You could sell it all to me! *Fine*

2nd position Now I'm small and a nick-el's all That I have to buy a pop-corn ball; But when I grow up If I ev-er do What a lot I'll buy from you. *D.C. al Fine*

D.C. (Da Capo) al fine means return to the beginning and play to Fine.

TWO "HAND POSITIONS"

This piece requires two "HAND POSITIONS" as shown here. Practice each pattern carefully.

ACCENT each note bearing this sign

First Position

Second Position

35. THE MERRY-GO-ROUND

I'm riding a kangaroo
When I'm not changing off to a gnu!
O, a merry-go-round is fun
For every age under the sun.

52

SYNCOPATION

Here is another recital piece, this time with the atmosphere of Old Spain. *Fiesta*, the Spanish word for holiday, is a time of processions, dancing, feasting and merry-making.

The TYING OVER of the LAST half of the first beat into the FIRST half of the second beat results in a RHYTHMICAL effect known as *syncopation*. The effect will be distinguished by giving a slight emphasis to the notes marked

TO LEARN THIS PIECE; first study the HARMONY PATTERN

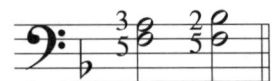

Then practice it in this form

Now become familiar with the RHYTHMICAL pattern in the right hand. It is practically the same in every measure. Be sure to emphasize the notes marked

The student should be able to clap or tap the rhythm before attempting to play.
Follow all expression marks.

Play with good, sharp rhythm and earn a place on the next recital program.

36. A SPANISH FIESTA

In the street dance see them whirl;
Gallant boy and dark-eyed girl,
I would love to be in Spain
When Fiesta comes again!

M.M. ♩ = 66 - 132

5640

Note to Teachers: *For additional practice rhythms, see "The HANON Studies" by John Thompson, page 22.*

37. THE FOX HUNT

(*A Hunting Song*)

Play cheerfully and with dash

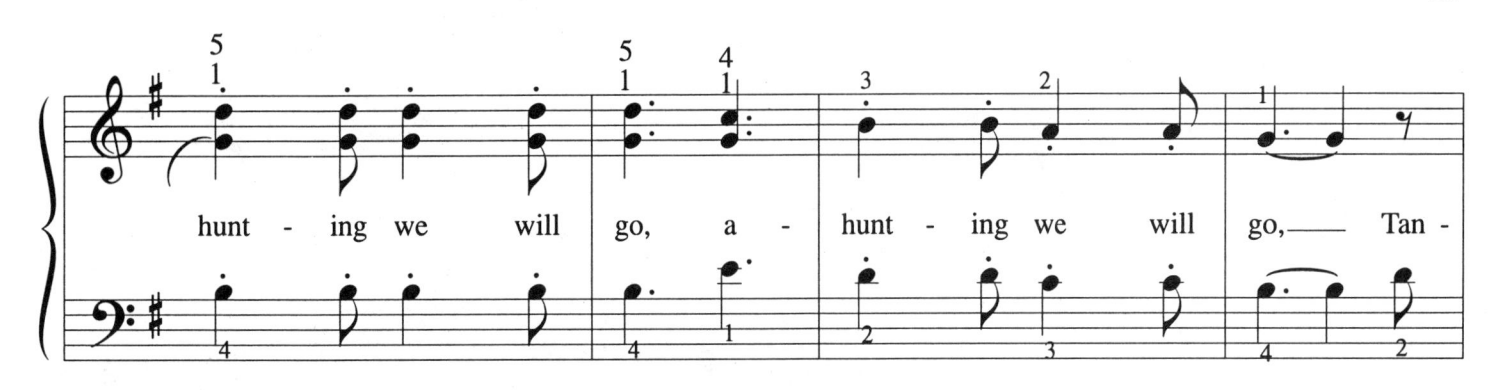

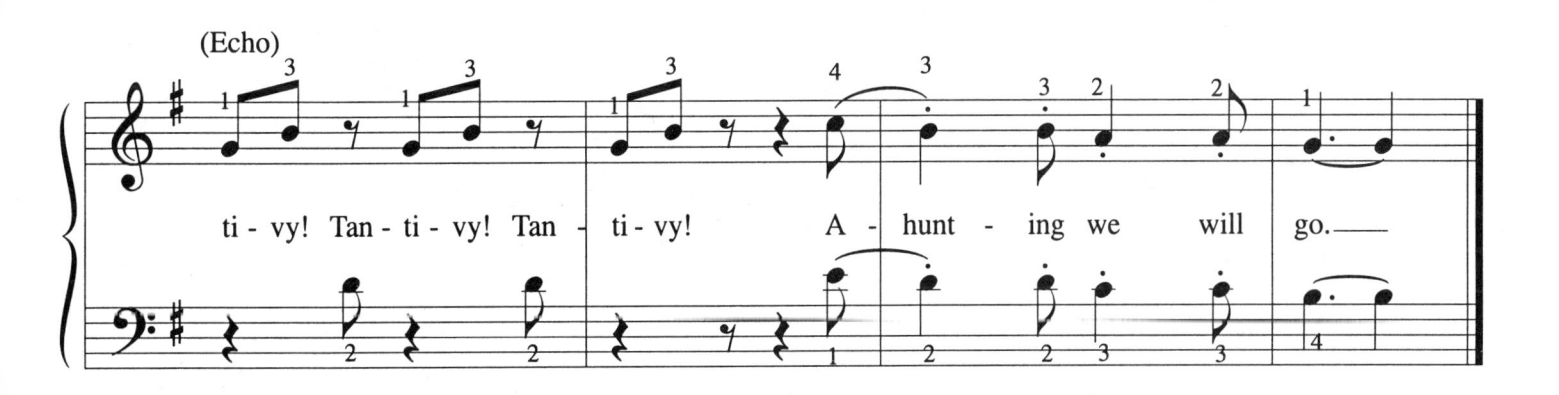

hunt-ing we will go, a - hunt-ing we will go,— Tan-ti-vy! Tan-ti-vy! Tan-ti-vy! A - hunt-ing we will go.— Tan-

pp

(Echo)

ti-vy! Tan-ti-vy! Tan-ti-vy! A - hunt-ing we will go.—

TWO "HAND POSITIONS"

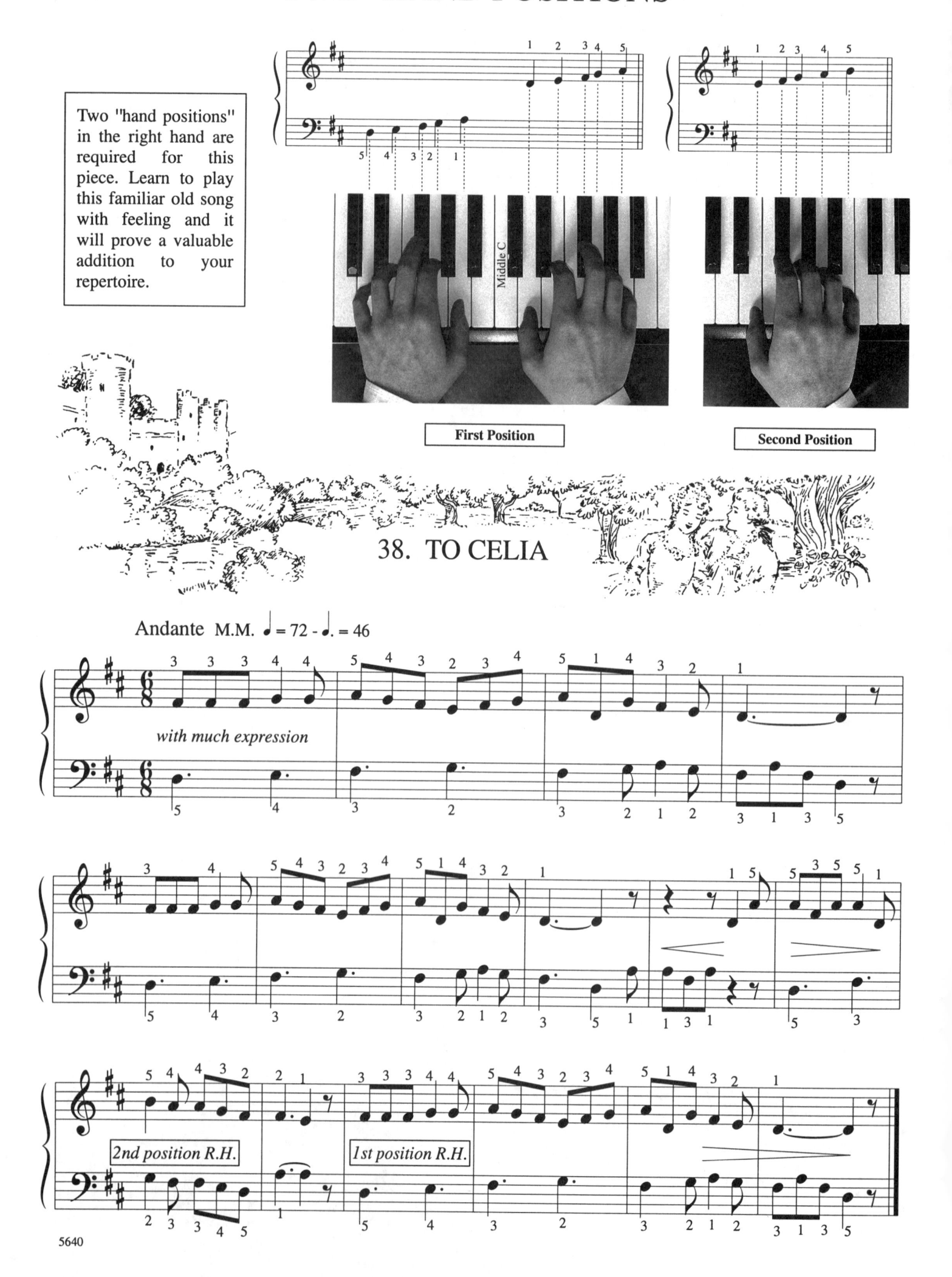

Two "hand positions" in the right hand are required for this piece. Learn to play this familiar old song with feeling and it will prove a valuable addition to your repertoire.

First Position

Second Position

38. TO CELIA

Andante M.M. ♩ = 72 - ♩. = 46

with much expression

2nd position R.H.

1st position R.H.

EXAMINATION No. 3

1. What is the meaning of this sign, ⌒ ?..

2. What is SYNCOPATION? ....

3. How much extra time is given to a DOTTED NOTE? ....

4. What should be uppermost when playing DANCE FORMS? ....

Grade on above ORAL examination ....

5. Play the following SCALES, first reciting the KEY SIGNATURE of each.

   Grade
   A major   ....
   G major   ....
   B flat major   ....
   F major   ....

   Average grade for SCALE playing ....

6. Play the following TRIADS in ROOT position, 1st INVERSION and 2nd INVERSION, naming each position.

   Grade
   A major   ....
   G major   ....
   B flat major   ....
   F major   ....

   Average grade for TRIAD playing .....

AVERAGE GRADE
for examination No. 3

Attach Certificate No. 3 here

5640

CROSS-HAND POSITION

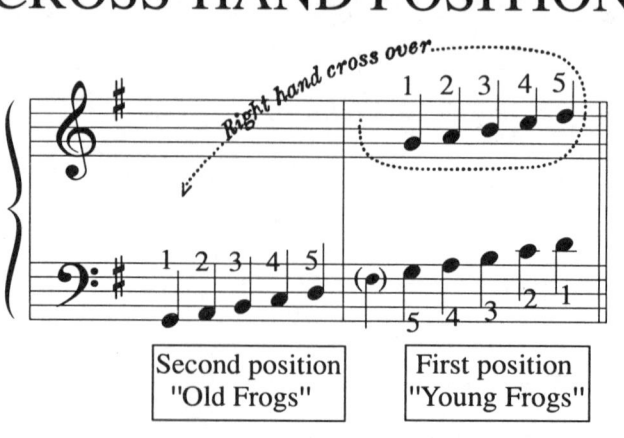

Second position "Old Frogs"   First position "Young Frogs"

Before attempting this piece place your hands in the G major position (first position above) and bring your right hand over to the second position above. Practice until the movement becomes quite natural.

39. THE FROG CHORUS

Over the lily pads
Froggies at play
Join in the chorus
To greet a new day.

Young frogs sing high
And the old frogs boom low,
All join the chorus
Their good will to show.

Suggestion for supplementary solo in sheet form

THE DUTCH TWINS by Willa Ward in the Key of C major is an unusually fine recital piece to stress interpretation. It also develops cross-hand playing.

WRIST STACCATO

Use a flexible, bouncing wrist when playing this piece and see how crisp you can make the STACCATO passages.

40. THE SLEIGH

Jingle, jingle, jingle,
In our sleigh we go,
Just like old Kris Kringle
Through the ice and snow.

Playfully M.M. ♩ = 56 - 88

p sharp staccato

Fine

D.C. al Fine

For students interested in keyboard harmony this example affords a splendid study in 2nd's and 3rd's. Underline all 2nd's. Draw circles around 3rd's.

5640

Key of E♭ Major
Signature
B♭ E♭ A♭

41. LITTLE BO-PEEP

Little Bo-Peep has lost her sheep
And looks for them sedately,
I wish she'd find them soon, because
We've had no lamb chops lately.

Andante moderato M.M. ♩ = 66 - ♩. = 50

Suggestion for supplementary solo in sheet form

COBBLER, COBBLER, a very attractive novelty in the Key of G major by Louise Christine Rebe, will prove a very interesting diversion.

5640

THE FOREARM ATTACK

The FOREARM attack is used in playing large chords. Shape the chord with the hand, allowing the fingers to rest gently on the tops of the keys. Then press forward from the elbow (*keeping the wrists loose*) and the effect will be a sustained tone of good singing quality.

HAND-POSITION
(Note *Extension in the right hand*)

HOW TO STUDY THIS PIECE

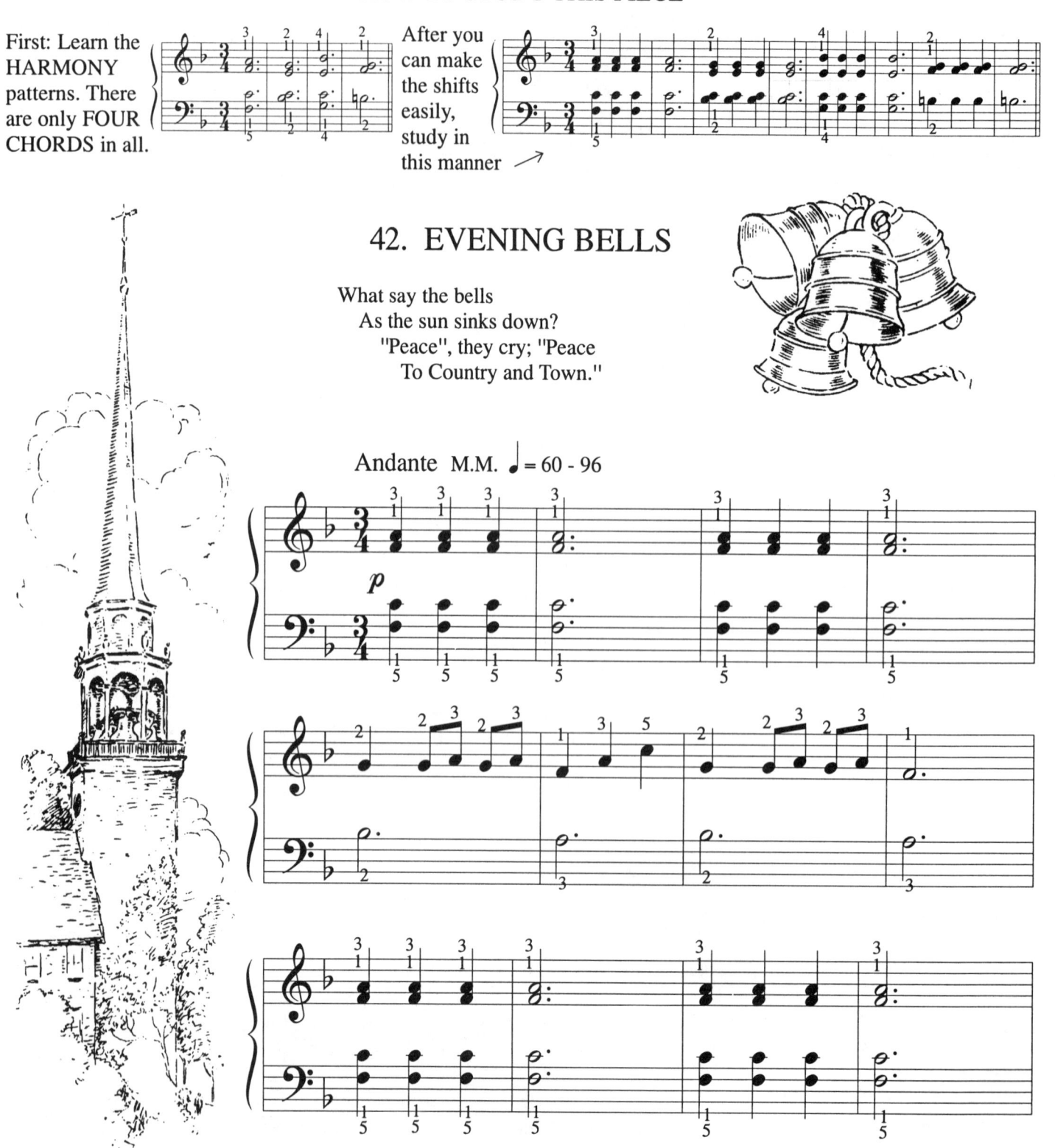

First: Learn the HARMONY patterns. There are only FOUR CHORDS in all.

After you can make the shifts easily, study in this manner

42. EVENING BELLS

What say the bells
As the sun sinks down?
"Peace", they cry; "Peace
To Country and Town."

Andante M.M. ♩ = 60 - 96

Note to Teachers: *For further development of the FOREARM ATTACK, see "The HANON Studies, Book One" by John Thompson, page 14.*

Key of E Major Signature
F# C# G# D#

In "PEASANT DANCE" the left hand part represents the drone of the bass viols which were often used to make the music to which the peasants danced on the village green.

43. PEASANT DANCE

All 'round the Maypole
Gather to-day,
 Crowning a Queen
Of the beautiful May.

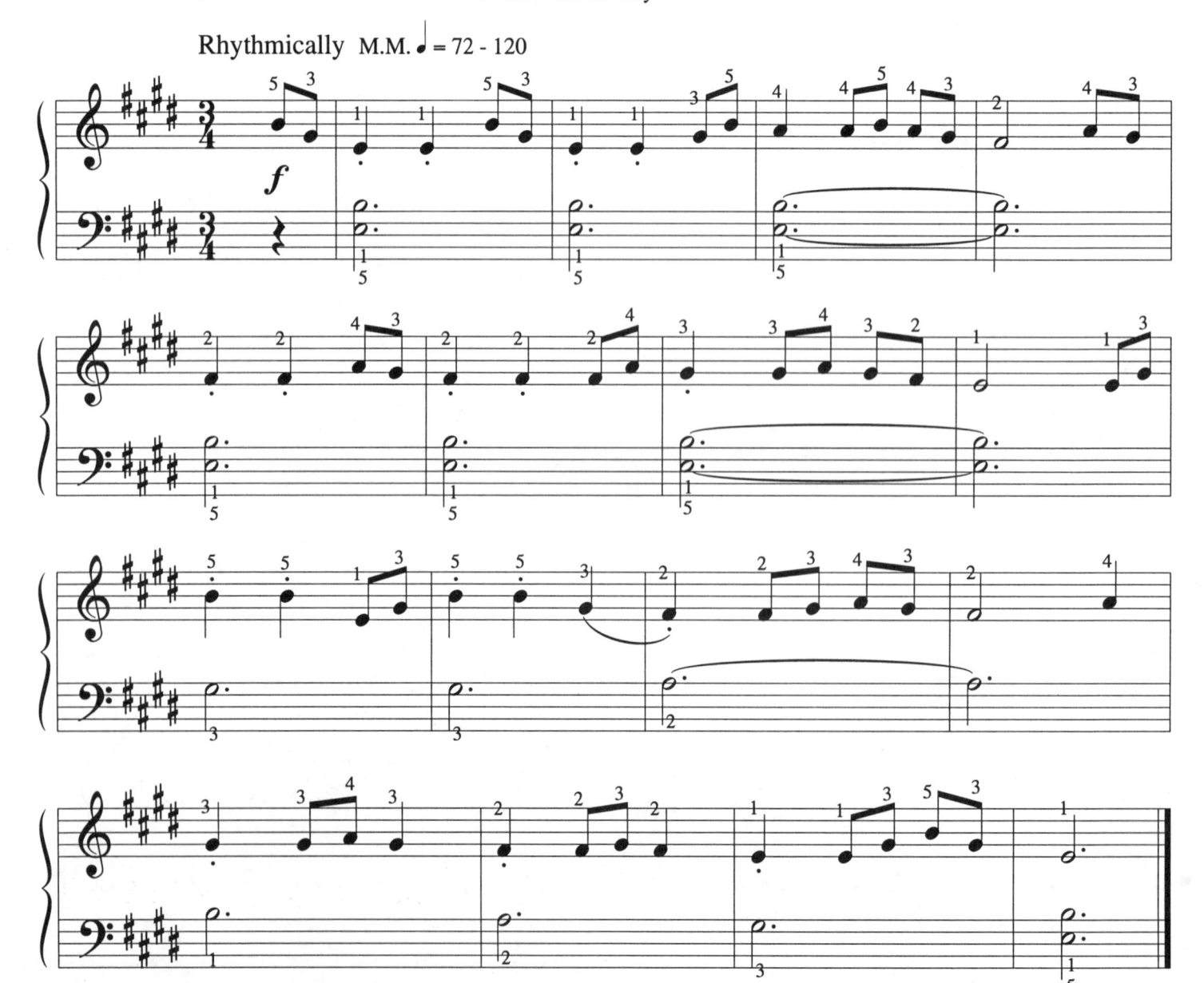

Rhythmically M.M. ♩ = 72 - 120

TWO "HAND POSITIONS"

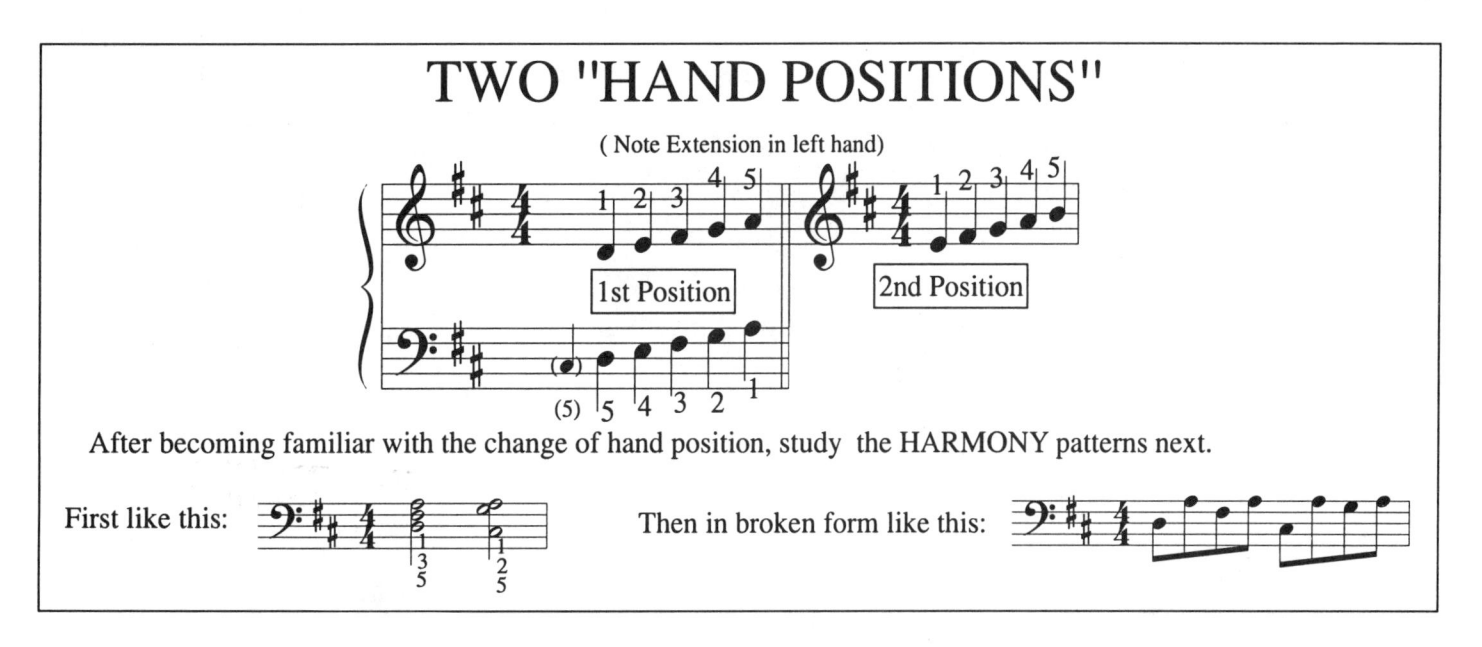

(Note Extension in left hand)

1st Position   2nd Position

After becoming familiar with the change of hand position, study the HARMONY patterns next.

First like this: Then in broken form like this:

44. LONG, LONG AGO

Thomas H. Bayly

Andante

Note to Teachers: "The HANON Studies" by John Thompson provides many useful examples in LEGATO and STACCATO.

THREE "HAND POSITIONS"

This traditional Christmas Carol requires three separate hand positions for the right hand and one position for the left hand. Practice the shift upward in all three positions to facilitate easy reading.

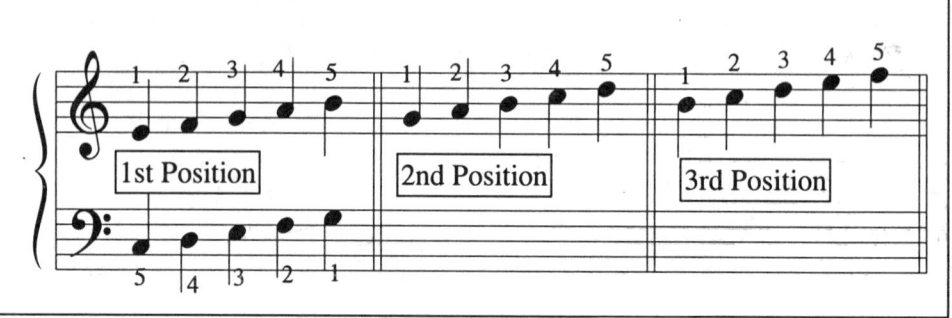

45. SILENT NIGHT

Franz Grüber

Andante M.M. ♩ = 104

THREE "HAND POSITIONS"—For both hands

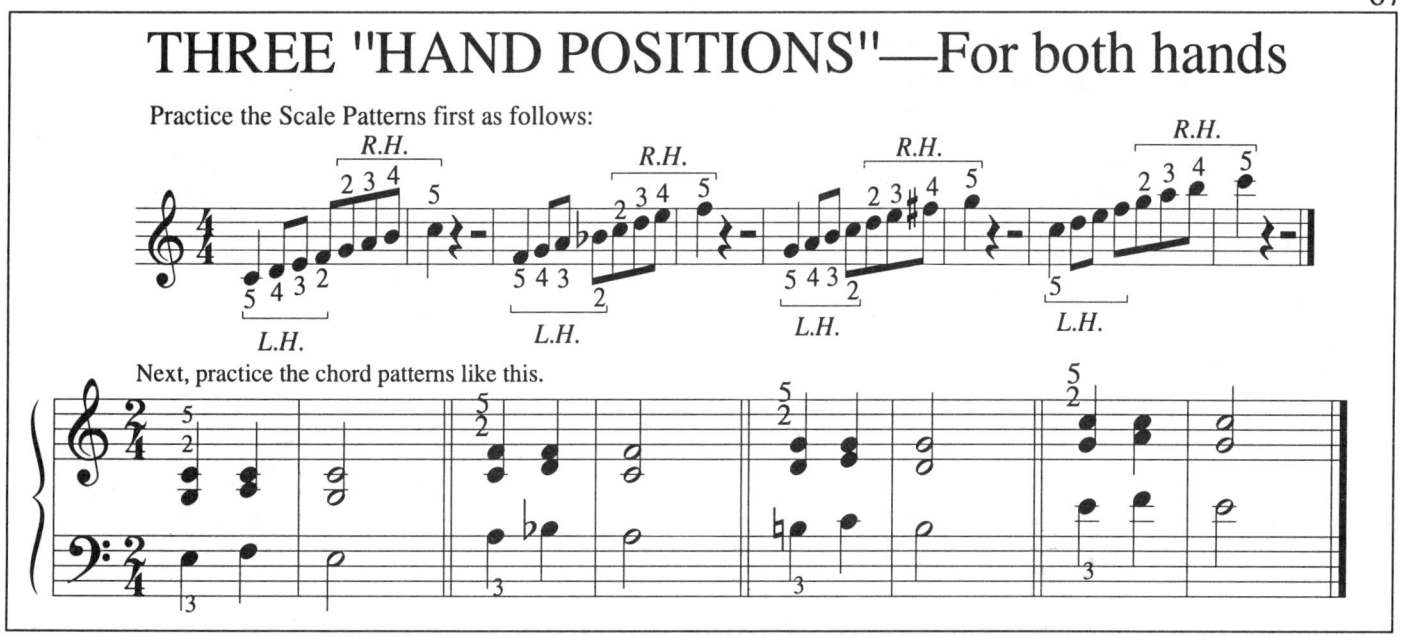

Practice the Scale Patterns first as follows:

Next, practice the chord patterns like this.

46. A KEYBOARD RECREATION

If you think you can't have fun
With Scale and Chord,
Just play this little piece!
Now, *were* you bored?

Allegro M.M. ♩ = 120

Try to interpret this characteristic piece so that the friends for whom you play will enjoy the illusion.
CAUTION: Watch the expression marks!

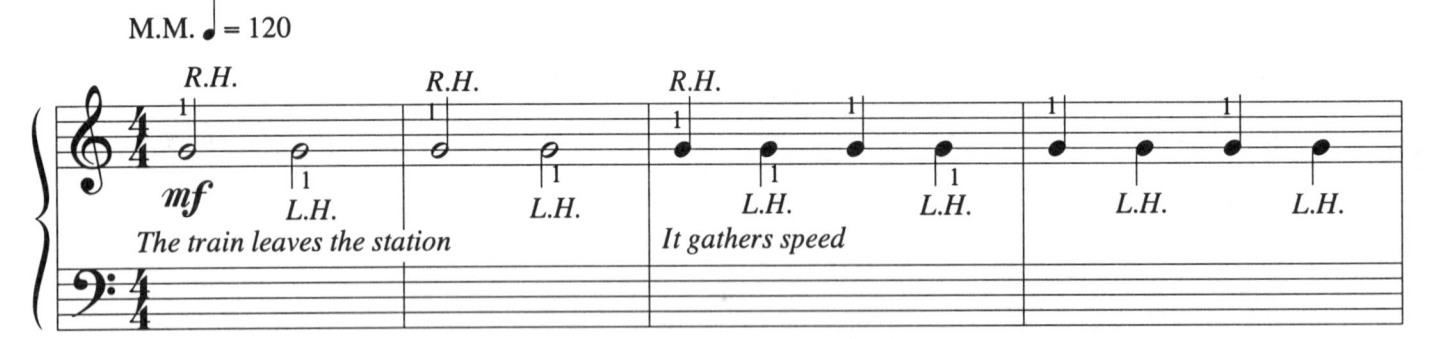

47. THE STREAMLINER

M.M. ♩ = 120

The train leaves the station / *It gathers speed*

The whistle blows   *and blows again*

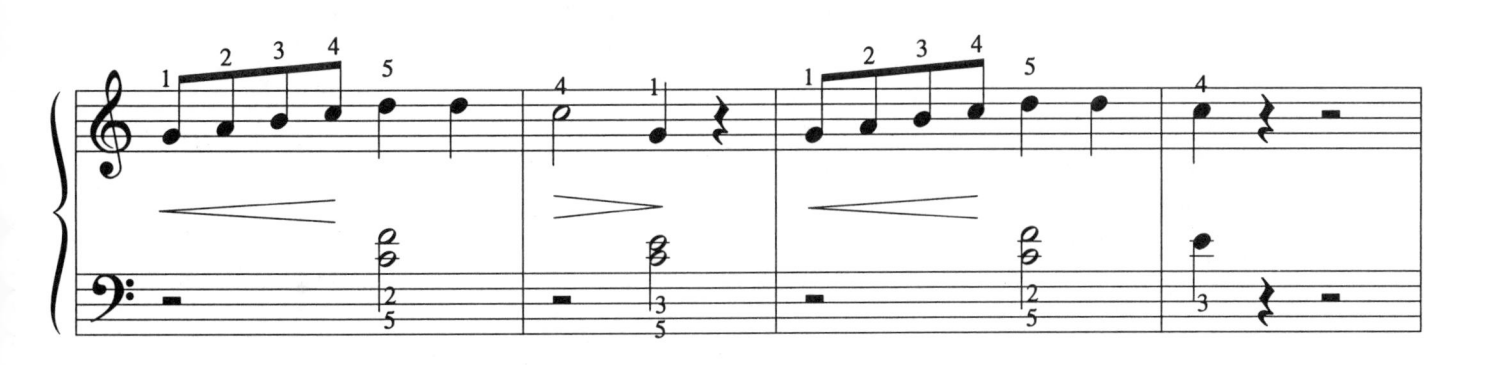

The train begins to slow down

Reaches journey's end.

Key of A♭ Major Signature B♭ E♭ A♭ D♭

NEW HAND POSITION

48. TO A SKYSCRAPER

How very strong you must be made
Not to be a bit afraid!
How can you there amid the clouds
Look down so calmly on the crowds?

71

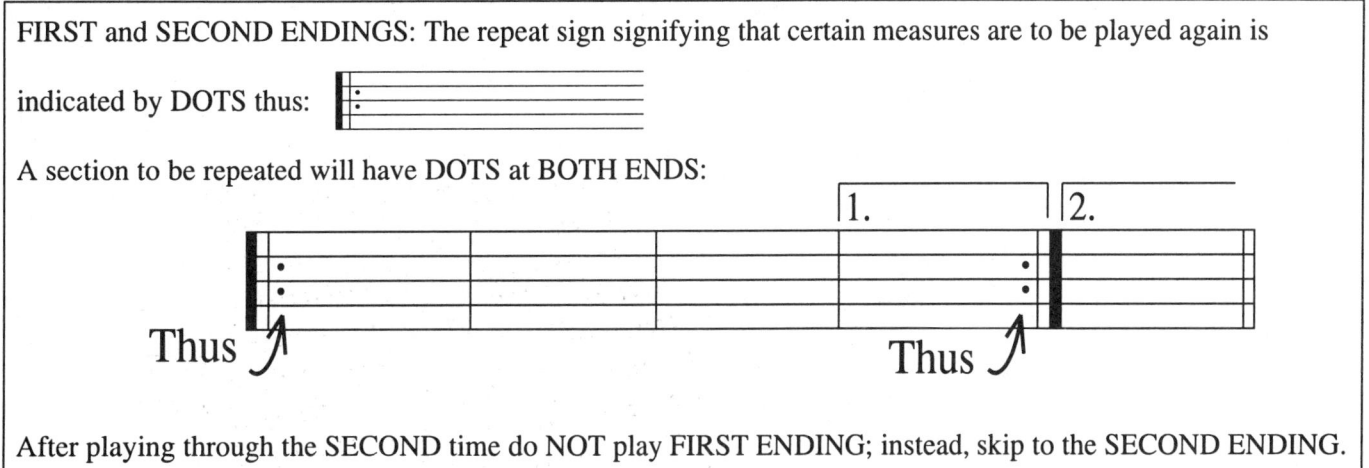

FIRST and SECOND ENDINGS: The repeat sign signifying that certain measures are to be played again is indicated by DOTS thus:

A section to be repeated will have DOTS at BOTH ENDS:

Thus

Thus

After playing through the SECOND time do NOT play FIRST ENDING; instead, skip to the SECOND ENDING.

5640

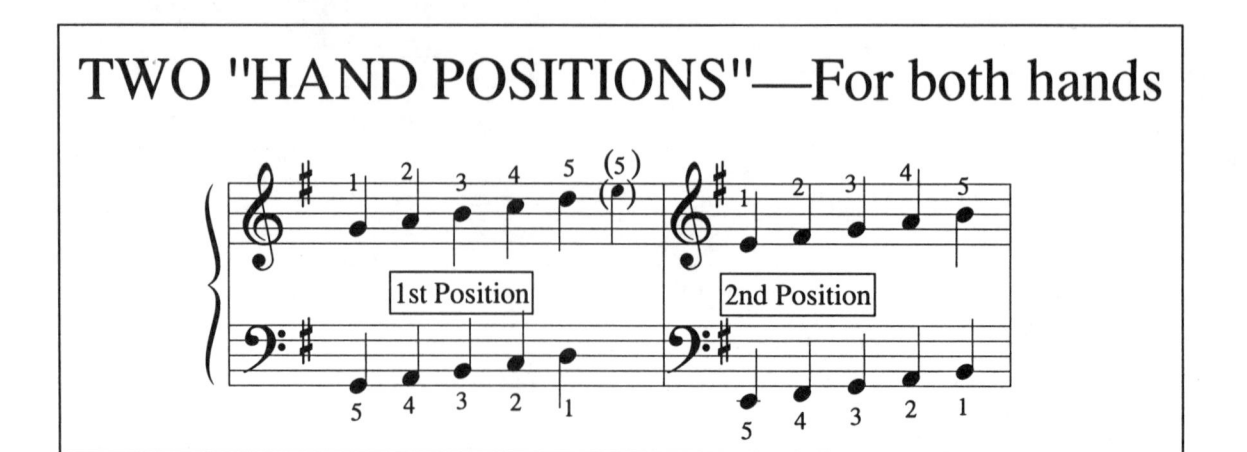

TWO "HAND POSITIONS"—For both hands

1st Position 2nd Position

49. DUBLIN TOWN

I would be goin' to Dublin Town
If I had new shoes and a velvet gown,
But since I have neither, I drive my pigs
And fill my time gaily with songs and jigs.

Lively M.M. ♩. = 76

mf 1st position

f 2nd position

Suggestions for supplementary solo in sheet form

THE BOGEY MAN, a rhythmic humoresque in C major, 6/8 Time by Lois Long, develops STACCATO and PHRASING.

SIXTEENTH NOTES

The TIME VALUE of Sixteenth notes is HALF that of EIGHTH notes. There are TWO sixteenth notes to one EIGHTH note and FOUR Sixteenth notes to one QUARTER note

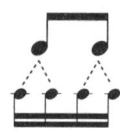

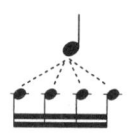

In this stirring piece your hands will be taken out of the FIVE-FINGER position, but if you observe the FINGER PATTERNS—1, 2, 3—3, 2, 1 it will be quite easy to master.

50. JOHN PEEL

D'ye ken John Peel with his coat so gay?
D'ye ken John Peel at the break of day?
D'ye ken John Peel when he's far away
With his hounds and his horn in the morning?

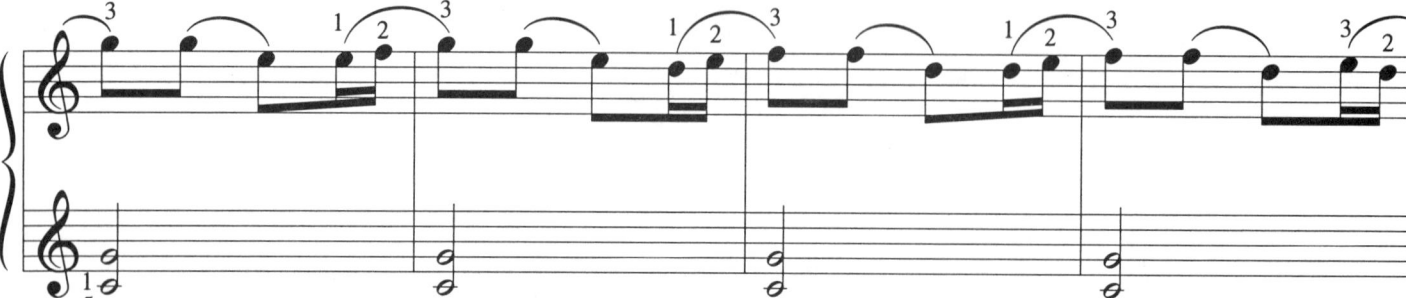

Scotch Folk Song

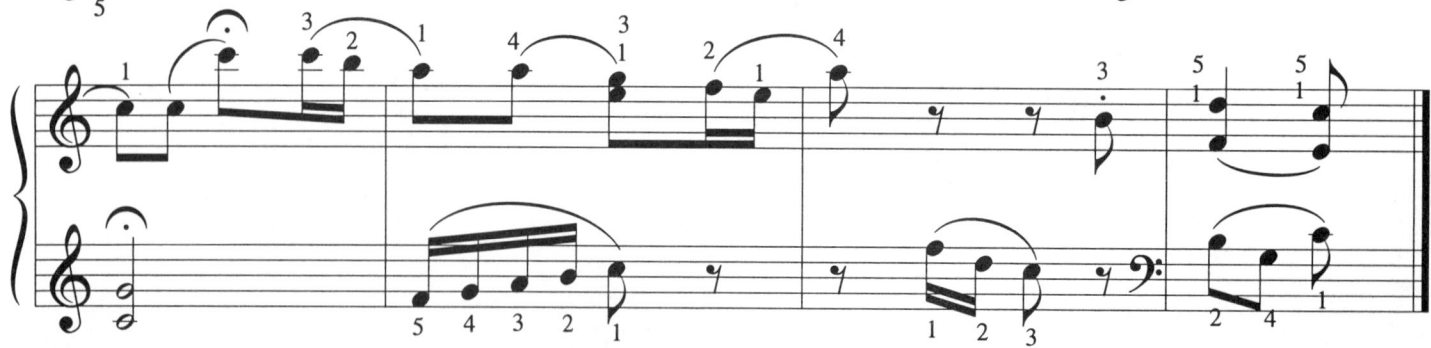

EXAMINATION No. 4

1. What is a NOCTURNE? ....

2. Explain 6-8 TIME ....

3. What does D.C. al FINE mean? ....

4. What is the value of a SIXTEENTH NOTE? ....

   Grade on above ORAL examination ....

5. Play the following SCALES, first reciting the KEY SIGNATURE of each.

   Grade
   - E flat major   ....
   - E major   ....
   - D major   ....
   - A flat major   ....

   Average grade for SCALE playing ....

6. Play the following TRIADS in ROOT position, 1st INVERSION and 2nd INVERSION, naming each position.

   Grade
   - E flat major   ....
   - E major   ....
   - D major   ....
   - A flat major   ....

   Average grade for TRIAD playing .....

AVERAGE GRADE
for examination No. 4

Attach Certificate No. 4 here

5640

TECHNICAL DRILLS

Note to Teachers: *Appended herewith are sixteen technical exercises for the development of fingers, arms and wrists, including some drills in two-note and three-note phrasing attack. They are intended for use during the study of this book. They may be assigned purely at the option of the teacher, who will be governed, naturally, by the capacity of the student. If used, they should be taught by rote. The teacher should play each one slowly as it is assigned and allow the student to learn the finger and rhythmical patterns, thus making it possible to transpose into any key. These drills will do much to facilitate keyboard mastery if given a little practice daily.*
First, each hand separately—then together, an octave apart.

Two-Finger Groups - The Trill

Three-Finger Groups

Four-Finger Groups

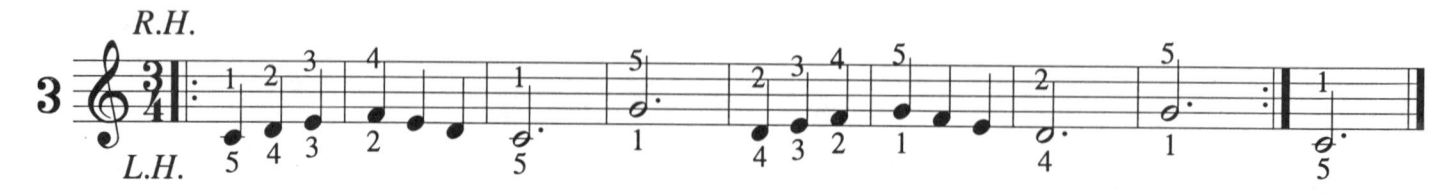

Five-Finger Groups

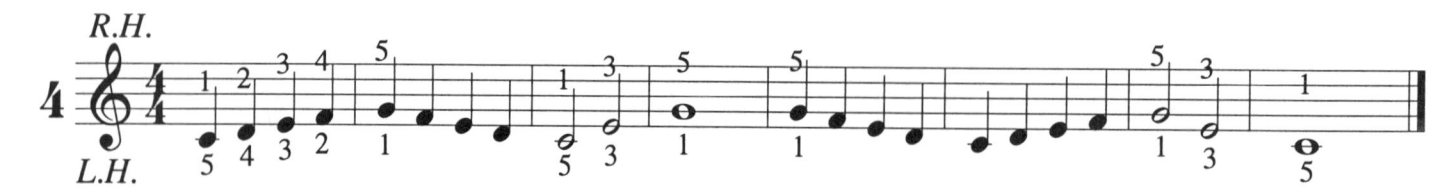

Two-Note Phrases
Drop-Roll

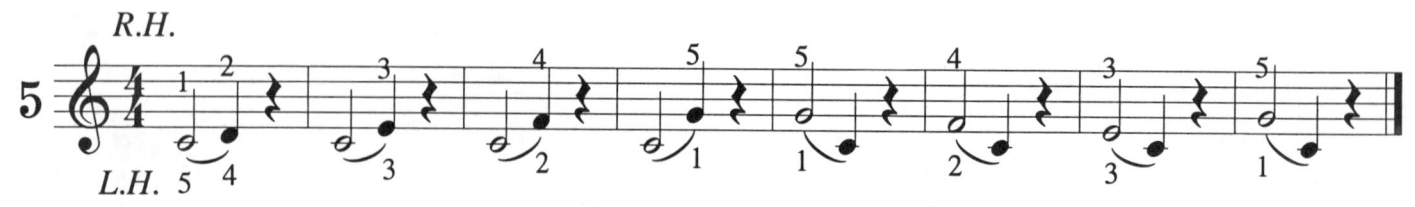

Three-Note Phrases
Drop-Connect-Roll

The Major Scale Divided between the Hands

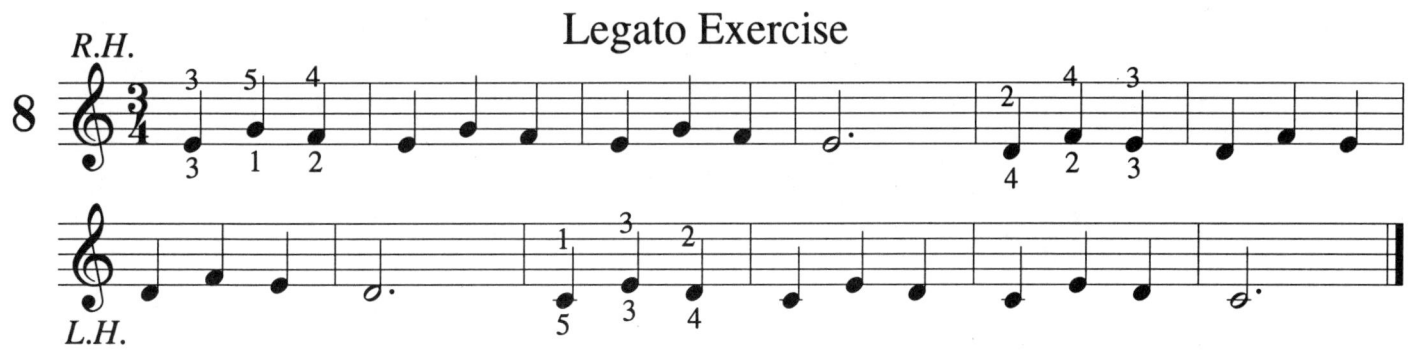

Legato Exercise

The Major Scale with Cadence Chords

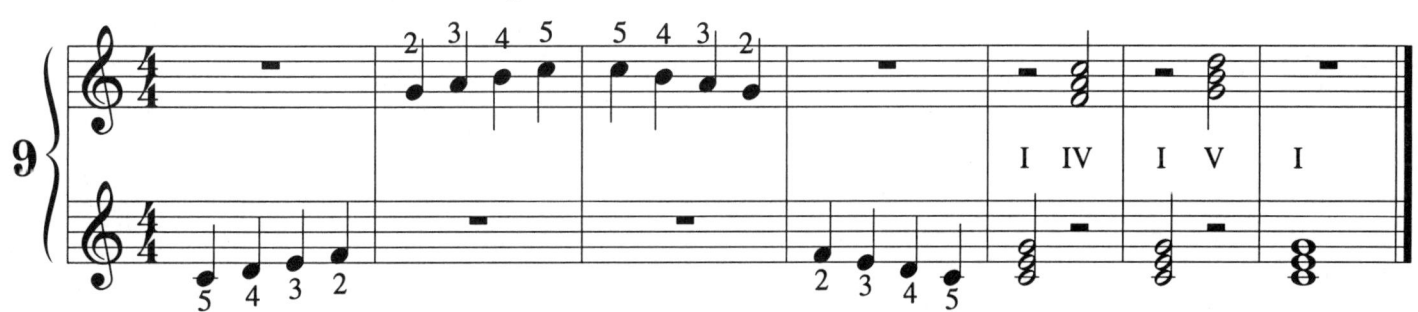

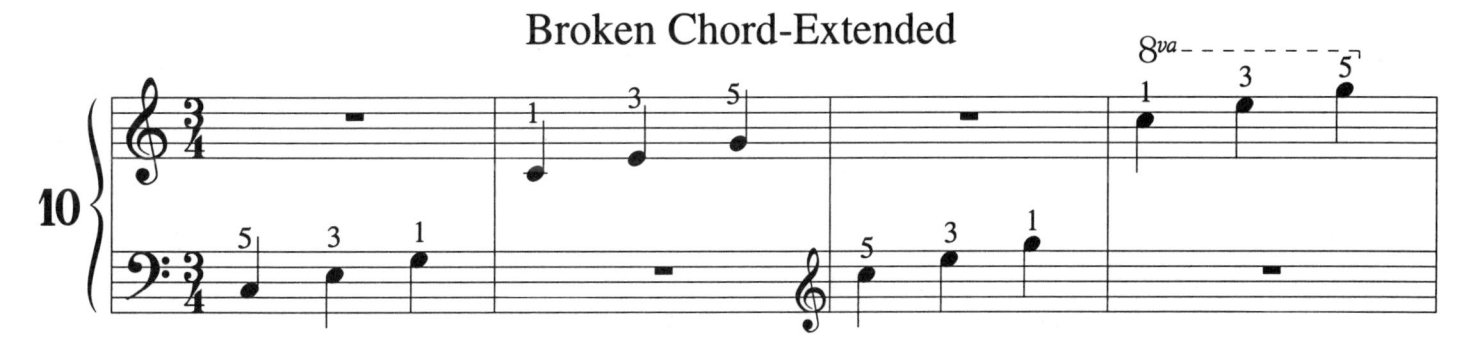

I   IV   I   V   I

Broken Chord-Extended

Broken Chord with Inversions

Broken Chord and Diatonic Figures Combined

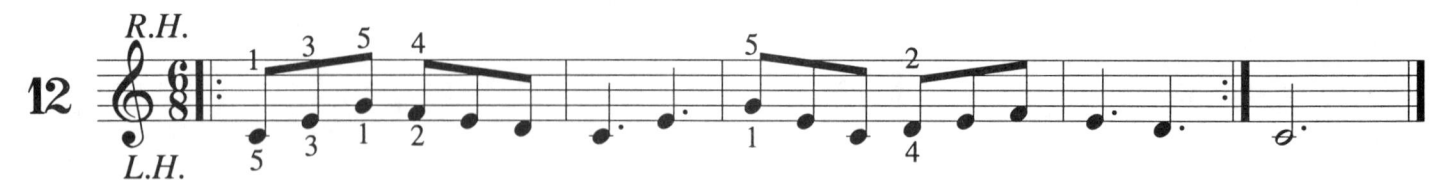

Ascending Finger Patterns

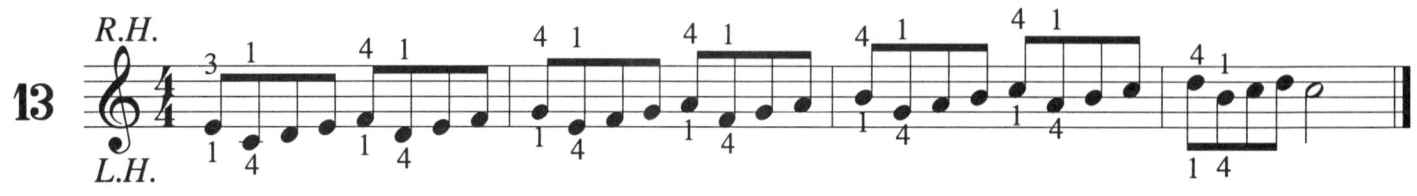

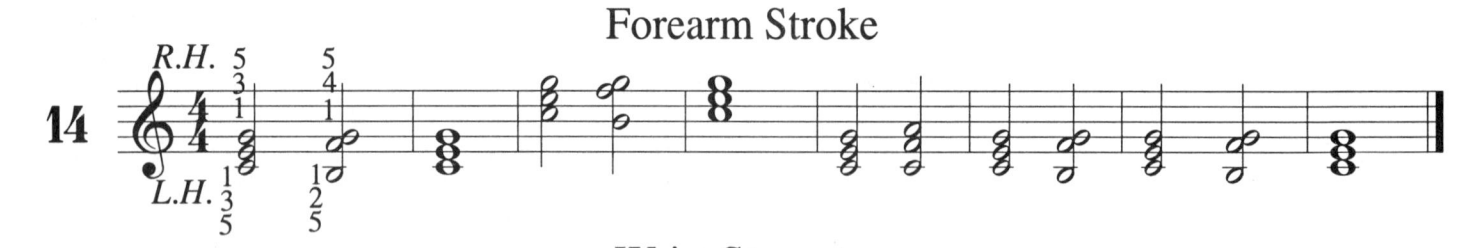

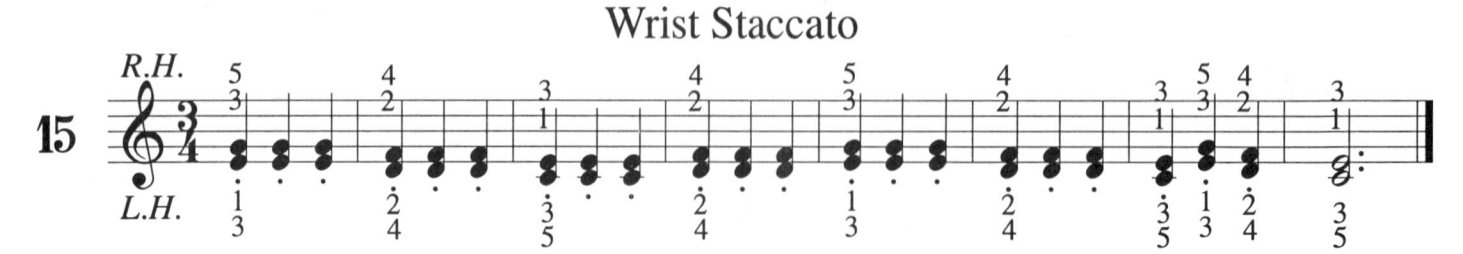

Forearm Stroke

Wrist Staccato

Broken Chord Drill Bugle Call

No. 4—Page 75

Certificate of Merit

This certifies that

....

has successfully passed
EXAMINATION No. 4

**THE FIRST GRADE BOOK
of
JOHN THOMPSON'S MODERN COURSE
FOR THE PIANO**

....
Teacher

Date......................

Seal

No. 3—Page 57

Certificate of Merit

This certifies that

....

has successfully passed
EXAMINATION No. 3

**THE FIRST GRADE BOOK
of
JOHN THOMPSON'S MODERN COURSE
FOR THE PIANO**

....
Teacher

Date......................

Seal

Certificate of Merit

This certifies that

....

has successfully passed
EXAMINATION No. 2

**THE FIRST GRADE BOOK
of
JOHN THOMPSON'S MODERN COURSE
FOR THE PIANO**

....
Teacher

Date......................

Seal

No. 2—Page 39

Certificate of Merit

This certifies that

....

has successfully passed
EXAMINATION No. 1

**THE FIRST GRADE BOOK
of
JOHN THOMPSON'S MODERN COURSE
FOR THE PIANO**

....
Teacher

Date......................

Seal

No. 1—Page 20

*Each certificate to be cut out and pasted on
respective page when earned by student*

Certificate of Merit

This certifies that

....

has successfully completed

"JOHN THOMPSON'S FIRST GRADE BOOK"

and is eligible for promotion to

"JOHN THOMPSON'S SECOND GRADE BOOK"

....
Teacher

Date........................

Seal — JOHN THOMPSON'S MODERN COURSE FOR PIANO

JOHN THOMPSON

Talented American pianist/composer John Thompson was born in Pennsylvania. At an early age he appeared as a concert pianist in all of the principal cities of America and Europe, where his brilliant playing received the highest praise. After concluding his triumphant concert career he headed music departments at conservatories in Philadelphia, Indianapolis and Kansas City. During these tenures he developed certain definite and original ideas about teaching, and in a short time became famous for his sincere efforts to interest young pupils in pianism. All of his books teach, in the simplest language possible, interpretation and expression. One ideal is "to use in miniature the same attacks as those used by the concert artist."

COMPOSITIONS FOR PIANO SOLO

#	Title	Grade	Key
4845	Air de Ballet, Op 43	3	E♭
5211	Castanets and Tambourines	3	Cm
4832	Columbine's Lament, Op 42, No 2	2	Gm
5201	Faun	3	G
4831	Harlequin, Op. 42, No.1	3	C
5354	Les Clochettes	3	G
5271	Midnight Express	3	G
4774	Moths	3	G
5349	Petite Russian Rhapsodie	3	C
5670	Plantation Memories	3	C
4952	Polliwog	3	Dm
5200	Skater	3	D
4829	Sparks	2	Dm
4993	Wings	3	A
5245	Young America	3	G

ARRANGEMENTS OF FAMOUS MELODIES

#	Title	Grade	Key
5277	Anitra's Dance (Grieg)	2.5	C
4911	Black Eyes (Russian Gypsy Folk-Song)	4	Dm
5204	Dream of Love (Liebesträume) (Liszt)	3.5	A♭
5231	Nocturne. Op. 23 (Schumann)	3	F
5229	On Wings of Song (Mendelssohn)	3	A♭
5279	Viennese Melody (Song Without Words)	3	G
5232	Waltz of the Flowers (from "The Nutcracker Suite," Tschaikowsky)	3	D

JOHN THOMPSON'S STUDENTS SERIES
PIANO SOLOS

GRADE I

#	Title	Composer	Key
5760	Barnyard Frolics	Blackford	G
5651	Cobbler, Cobbler	Rebe	G
5652	The Dutch Twins	Ward	C
5672	Forest Dawn	Thompson	C
5653	Hoe Cake Shuffle	Leslie	G
5784	In The Swing	Waldo	C
5648	Lullaby (Brahms)	Thompson	G
5650	March of the Spooks	Haines	Cm
5647	Marche Slave (Tschaikowsky)	Thompson	Am
5656	Moccasin Dance	Long	Am
5745	On the Levee	Waldo	C
5655	Procession of the Seven Dwarfs	Long	G
5657	Swaying Silver Birches	Leslie	C
5790	Twilight Lullaby	Haines	C

GRADE II

#	Title	Composer	Key
6337	The Banjo Picker	Wright	A
5724	Busy Corners	Montandon	C
5668	The Brownies Carnival	Thompson	C
5664	Captain Kidd	Waldo	Gm
5721	The Cheer Leader	Rodgers	C
5723	The Dirigible	Thompson	G
5785	Dreamy Time Song	Munn	F
5666	Drowsy Moon	Long	G
5663	Hiawatha's Lullaby	Ward	G
5669	On a Summer Sea	Ketterer	C
5726	Parade of the Penguins	Wade	Am
5719	Roguish Eyes	Haines	G
5665	The Swan on the Moonlit Lake	Rebe	G
5792	Swinging High and Low	Cobb	D
5747	Under Southern Skies	Martin	C
5709	Woods at Dawn	Kerr	F

GRADE III

#	Title	Composer	Key
5717	Balloons	Arlen	A♭
5674	By a Roadside Fire	Rodgers	F
5722	The Drum Major	Selby	G
5665	March of the Champions	Waldo	G
5671	Tango Carioca	Thompson	Gm
5786	Three Blind Mice (Variations on the Theme)	Thompson	G-Gm-B♭
5720	The Wounded Gladiator	Long	Cm

PIANO FOUR HANDS

#	Title	Composer
5690	Down the Shady Path	Jenkins
5687	Flame Vine	Bilbro
5688	In the Morning Early	Jenkins
5791	Spirit of the U.S.A.	Cobb
5689	The Strolling Players	Jenkins
5718	Tulip Time	Broaddus

Published by **THE WILLIS MUSIC CO.** Florence, Kentucky 41022-0548

5640